FROM GEORGE TO GEORGE

★

*Presidential Elections in the United States
from 1789 to the Present*

From George to George

Presidential Elections in the United States
from 1789 to the Present

★

CURATED BY

R. Hal Williams & Hervey A. Priddy

Bridwell Library

SOUTHERN METHODIST UNIVERSITY ★ DALLAS, TEXAS ★ 2004

CATALOGING-IN-PUBLICATION DATA
From George to George: Presidential elections in the United States from
1789 to the present / curated by R. Hal Williams and Hervey A. Priddy ;
foreword by James A. McMillin.
Dallas, TX : Bridwell Library, 2004.
   p. cm.
ISBN 0-941881-33-4
1. Elections—United States—History. 2. Political parties—United States—
History. 3. Presidents—United States—Election—Miscellanea. 4. Political
collectibles—United States—Catalogs. 5. Campaign paraphernalia—United
States—Catalogs. 6. Bridwell Library—Exhibitions. I. Williams, R. Hal.
II. Priddy, Hervey A. III. McMillin, James A. IV. Bridwell Library.
E176.1 .W54 2004

ITEM 1
Andrew Jackson
textile, 1829
inauguration.

Table of Contents

List of Illustrations

ITEM 3

William McKinley & Theodore Roosevelt "Hamilton County Republican Candidates" poster, 1900 election.

Foreword

★

JAMES A. McMILLIN

IN 2001 DALLAS NATIVE HERVEY A. PRIDDY DONATED HIS SUPERB COLLECTION of American campaign materials to Bridwell Library. Given Bridwell Library's specialties in early rare books and manuscripts—which are, of necessity, mainly European—many people might suppose that the gift signaled the Library's entry into the New World and a new field for acquisitions. Not so. Bridwell has strong American holdings in the areas of Bible, philosophy, early American printing, literature, Methodism, fine printing, and binding. Moreover, during the last half of the twentieth century, Bridwell Library acquired numerous campaign artifacts, the most noteworthy of which can be found in the Dan Ferguson Collection and the Decherd Turner Americana Collection. This most recent addition, which forms the nucleus of the Hervey A. Priddy Collection of American Presidential and Political Memorabilia, however, did greatly enlarge and enhance Bridwell's resources in the field. Numbering more than 250 items, the Priddy Collection contains a wide range of political materials, including printed works, textiles, ceramics, novelties, numismatics, and, of course, buttons from the early nineteenth century to the present.

These fascinating artifacts record the history of the most quintessential of American institutions, the presidential campaign. To better understand the phenomenon and in recognition of the 2004 campaign, Bridwell Library of the Perkins School of Theology at Southern Methodist University has mounted the exhibition *From George to George: Presidential Elections in the United States from 1789 to the Present*. The exhibition is curated by R. Hal Williams, Professor of American History, Southern Methodist University, and collector and benefactor Hervey A. Priddy. It explores significant themes in past presidential campaigns through historical documents, illustrations, paintings, and a wide range of campaign memorabilia.

Items are drawn from the holdings at Bridwell Library, including the recent gifts of Hervey A. Priddy. We have also borrowed important items from American Historical Autographs; the Amon Carter Museum; the Harlan Crow Library; the Museum of American Political Life; the Smithsonian Institution, National Museum of American History, Behring Center; and the Fondren and DeGolyer Libraries at SMU. We are grateful for their support. Several local collectors also have lent rare items to the exhibition. Lawrence

ITEM 4
George Washington
brass clothing button,
1789 inauguration.

Budner, Dr. Sandra Craig, Thomas J. Knock, Cary M. Maguire, and H. Ross Perot, Sr. have been especially generous. It was a pleasant surprise to discover that Dallas is a center for collectors of American political campaign material.

The making of this exhibition would not have been possible without the cooperation, generosity, and hard work of many people. We are most grateful to the curators of the exhibition and authors of the essays published here, R. Hal Williams and Hervey A. Priddy. We also thank Michelle Nickerson, who assisted in the research and writing of the exhibition labels. In our work with lending institutions, we were helped by a number of individuals: Harlan Crow and Ryan Lord of the Harlan Crow Library; Marianne Curling of the Museum of American Political Life, University of Hartford; Lisa Kathleen Graddy of the Smithsonian Institution, National Museum of American History, Behring Center; Rebecca Lawton of the Amon Carter Museum; and Joe Rubinfine of American Historical Autographs.

This catalogue would not have been possible without the generous support of Frost Bank, which has underwritten the cost of publication. We appreciate the support and goodwill of the people at Frost Bank, especially Linda Baker, Hardie Herman, James Johnston, Beverly Patrick, and Sue Turnage. The exhibition and the events in conjunction with it are also supported by the William P. Clements Department of History and the John G. Tower Center for Political Studies at SMU. Thanks to James Hopkins, Chair of the History Department, and James Hollifield, Director of the Tower Center, we can claim that this has been a collaborative effort at SMU.

We also acknowledge the hard work of our Bridwell Library colleagues. Our thanks go to Director Valerie Hotchkiss, who agreed to exhibit buttons instead of books; Page Thomas and Eric White, whose bibliographic knowledge was invaluable; Hermann Michaeli, who expertly organized the materials; Dennis Maust, our Public Programs Manager; Jon Speck, who orchestrated the beautiful display in the galleries; Jace Graf, who designed the catalogue; and the many others who helped along the way, especially Clayton Crenshaw, Jane Elder, Andrew Eubanks, Ellen Frost, Sally Hoover, Megan McLemore, Wanda Smith, Gayla Tennison, and Linda Umoh. Outside the library, we thank our SMU colleagues Martha Coniglio, Curt Holleman, Cal Jillson, Patricia Ann LaSalle, Glenn Linden, Russell Martin, Noëlle McAlpine, Mildred Pinkston, Sam Ratcliffe, Dennis Simon, and Harold Stanley. We also wish to thank Bill Grumbles, Amy Heitzman, and Tom Karsch for their assistance with the film festival that complements the exhibition, *The American Presidency: Fact, Fiction, and Film.* We are honored that two significant figures in the history of American politics, David Eisenhower and George McGovern, will participate in a lecture series at Bridwell Library in conjunction with the exhibition.

Thomas Jefferson once said, "Politics are such a torment that I would advise every one I love not to mix with them." We are not advising you to "mix with" politics as a politician, but we can recommend highly that you spend a few hours surveying those torments, as well as the trials and triumphs of American political campaigning that you will find in this exhibition and catalogue.

JAMES A. McMILLIN
Associate Director
Bridwell Library

ITEM 5

Caleb Bingham, *Stump Speaking*, c. 1850s.

From George to George

Presidential Elections in the United States from 1789 to the Present

★

R. HAL WILLIAMS

A PHYSICIAN, AN ENGINEER, AND A POLITICIAN were arguing once about whose profession was the most important. "Mine is," the physician said. "God created Eve from Adam's rib; that meant surgery, so we physicians were there at the creation." "No, no," the engineer said. "Take one step back. God created the universe from chaos. It was the greatest engineering feat in history. We engineers had to have been there at the creation." "Fair enough," the politician replied. "But who do you think created the chaos?"[1]

Americans have long had doubts about their politicians and political system, doubts we often think of as modern, but which go back in fact to the Founding Fathers and before. Yet there also has been an abiding faith in the principles of democracy, and democracy, as a number of observers have pointed out, is our country's most distinguishing characteristic and its vital contribution to world history.[2]

"America," Jane Addams, the early twentieth-century social settlement reformer, once said, is the "most daring experiment in democratic government which the world has ever seen."

The idea of democracy emerged in strength in the early nineteenth century, and once it did, it spread worldwide, at least in the hopes of people everywhere. Nothing guaranteed its emergence nor its continuance even today. "Appreciating its historically contingent nature," one scholar has noted, "allows us to recognize how breathtaking its arrival was, how extraordinary its spread has been, and how uncertain its prospects are."[3]

"POLITICS ARE MUCH DISCUSSED...," Charles Dickens noted on his visit to the United States in the early 1840s. Election campaigns seemed to be going on all the time, with one common feature: as soon as the arguments over the last election were over, arguments over the next one began, "which is an unspeakable comfort," Dickens remarked, "to all politicians and true lovers of their country: that is to say, to ninety-nine men and boys out of every ninety-nine and a quarter."[4]

*1844
Henry Clay
Medalet*

Dickens was right. In this land across the ocean politics almost never went away.

Elections took place around the year, not just those for president or Congress, but for a host of positions—an election of one kind or another just about every month in the calendar.

New Jersey, to take one example, had statewide elections in March, April, May, and December; other states did the same, and then there were district, county, city, and ward elections. Each election had its own party meetings and conventions; each had its own period of campaigning and voting.5

"We work through one campaign," a tired Iowa politician once complained, "take a bath, and start in on the next."6

"[T]he political activity that pervades the United States must be seen in order to be understood," Alexis de Tocqueville, another famous visitor, noted. "No sooner do you set foot upon American ground than you are stunned by a kind of tumult; a confused clamor is heard on every side, and a thousand simultaneous voices demand the satisfaction of their social wants."7

Tocqueville did not note it, but in the United States, politics and economics form a peculiarly American linkage. Voting and the market are perhaps the two most important means ever devised of reaching collective decisions through individual choices.8

It is no surprise, then, that through the first century-and-a-half of our history, people were devoted to their political party. It gave them identity, defined social relationships, provided a way to take part in the democratic process, and offered some stake in a better future. It did something more as well. In an extraordinarily mobile society, political parties transcended state and territorial borders, and people moving into new areas could carry with them the party slogans, rituals, and identifications they had known back home. They adjusted to the new, in short, by taking with them important parts of the old.

Elections, candidates, and campaigns, therefore, as this exhibition shows, tell us a great deal about the nature of our democracy, culture, and political system.

Using an array of fascinating campaign memorabilia—flags, posters, vases, torches, buttons, and paintings, among many others—this exhibition traces the course of our elective democracy from "George to George," from George Washington in 1789 to George W. Bush in 2004. These mementos, one should remember, stir with life. Living hands once touched them; living minds once identified intensely with them; living hearts once hoped they would bring victory to their cause.

2000
George W. Bush
Badge

YET THERE ARE SOME TODAY who wonder if our political system itself is still living.

Nearly everyone of a certain age can remember when most people they knew voted, when schoolchildren wore campaign buttons and shouted campaign slogans, when party workers nailed posters to telephone poles or taped them to store windows, and when political leaflets were slipped under windshield wipers.

Most of these things, of course, are no longer true.

Voter turnout, one measure of the change, has dropped dramatically. Only half of the country's eligible voters currently show up at the polls for presidential elections. In state and local contests, only twenty or twenty-five percent do so; in municipal or village elections, it may be fewer than ten percent. A runoff election in a 1998 statewide Texas primary brought three percent of the electorate to the polls.9

Turnout nationwide is now the lowest it has been since 1840, more than a century-and-a-half ago.[10] Even after the tragic events of 11 September 2001, when many officials urged voters to come out in great numbers to show the world that democracy remained strong, relatively few people came. In New York City itself, one site of the tragedy, only thirty-six percent of registered voters showed up that fall at the polls.[11]

Or, to look at the same phenomenon another way: if sixty-three percent of the electorate had voted in the year 2000, as they did as recently as the Kennedy-Nixon election of 1960, nearly twenty-five million more people would have gone to the polls, a number that if they had started at a voting booth in New York City, the line would have stretched across the country to Los Angeles and back, *twice over*.[12]

In 1974 Congress placed a box on personal income tax returns that allowed citizens to contribute to candidates' campaigns. At the time, one in three taxpayers checked it. Now, it is only one in eight.[13]

IN THINKING ABOUT THE HISTORY of our presidential elections, it can help to keep in mind some of the ways in which historians and political scientists have come to view them.

1884
James G. Blaine
Brooch

One way, helpful in distinguishing one election from another, is to classify them by effect. Scholars, as they often do, have applied different labels, but many refer to "maintaining," "deviating," and "realigning" elections. A "maintaining" election, as the name suggests, tends to reaffirm patterns of partisan attachment. A "deviating" election results in a temporary defeat of the party in power without altering the basic division of partisan loyalties, and a "realigning" election, in some ways the most important of all, changes the fundamental party commitments of a large portion of the electorate, who will vote differently in the future.[14]

"Maintaining" elections—the victories of Ulysses S. Grant in 1868 and 1872, William McKinley in 1900, Franklin D. Roosevelt, also known as FDR, in 1936 and after, George H. W. Bush in 1988, among others—are fairly obvious. "Deviating" elections include the victories of Democrat Woodrow Wilson in 1912 and 1916, a time of Republican hegemony, and Republican Dwight D. Eisenhower in 1952, in the midst of a Democratic era. "Realigning" elections, those that shift voting patterns for years to come, include the elections of 1800, 1828, 1860, 1896, and 1932.[15]

In recent years, some observers have argued, there may have begun a different kind of "realigning" election, a "philosophical" realignment, in which deep skepticism about the role of government in our society has replaced the pro-government attitude dating from the New Deal. The victories of Ronald Reagan in 1980 and 1984 could be evidence of this change, as was, perhaps, the Republican sweep of the 1994 Congressional elections under the slogan of a "Contract with America."[16]

Another way to help understand our elections has emerged in the recent work of scholars who have found in our political history five eras, or "party systems," periods of relatively stable patterns of voting that changed only during a "realigning" phase.[17]

The first party system, in this view, lasted from 1789 to the early 1820s and witnessed the initial steps toward the establishment of lasting party organizations. Since the steps were both halting and incomplete, some have called it "a *preparty* system."[18]

Running from about 1828 to the great realignment of the 1850s, the second party system witnessed the shift from strong local alignments into full two-party competition across the entire country, mainly between the Democrats and the Whigs. The third party system, lasting from the 1850s to the early 1890s, was the Civil War system that emerged from the collapse of the Whigs, the breakdown of nationwide partisan competition, and the reorganization of the party system along explicitly sectional lines.

The fourth party system, occurring from the early 1890s to about 1932, reflected the challenges of an increasingly urban-industrial society, punctuated particularly by a massive economic depression in the 1890s. Its hallmarks included Republican hegemony nationwide, one-party domination in both North and South, and a sharp decline in the enormous turnouts that had characterized the third party system. Finally, the fifth party system, often named the New Deal system, grew from the Great Depression and the partisan realignments of the 1930s. Two-party competition gradually re-emerged in one-party areas; class cleavages sharpened.[19]

One of the fascinating things about our national life today is that we are in the midst of a fierce battle for party control, the outcome of which historians will someday call the sixth party system.

★ II ★

IN GENERAL THE "FOUNDING FATHERS" loved freedom but doubted democracy, fearful of what might happen if ordinary people were placed in charge of the country's affairs.

"[T]he proposition that [the people] are the best keepers of their liberties is not true," John Adams, our second president, said in 1787. "They are the worst conceivable; they are no keepers at all. They can neither act, judge, think, or will...."[20]

That was pretty strong talk—shared, by the way, by men like George Washington, Alexander Hamilton, and Thomas Jefferson—and the talk grew stronger still when it came to political parties. The colonial elite feared the idea of political parties most of all. These harmful things, they were sure, fostered disorder, resisted control, acted from personal and selfish motives, and followed unpredictable purposes. Parties also would get in the way of the crucial task of nation-building, splitting people into separate camps at precisely the time when national unity was the foremost goal.[21]

"If I could not go to heaven but with a party," Jefferson famously said, "I would not go at all."[22]

Others would not go, too, especially the most celebrated individual of them all, the very "Father of his Country," who in his famous Farewell Address warned his countrymen solemnly against "the baneful effects of the Spirit of Party...." "It serves," he said, "always to distract the Public Councils and enfeeble the Public administration. It agitates the Community with ill founded jealousies and false alarms, kindles the animosity of one part against another, foments occasionally riot and insurrection."[23]

It was no surprise, then, that many early state constitutions included provisions that sought to make parties unnecessary, and the authors of the Constitution itself tried by indirection to do pretty much the same. The Constitution, as they wrote it, provided only the barest of electoral machinery and contained no mention whatever of political parties, nominating conventions, or other practical devices. It delegated to state legislatures the power to establish the eligibility of voters, while reserving to Congress only the authority to "make or alter such Regulations."[24]

On the eve of the Revolution, the electorate was adult, male, largely Protestant, and white. Even that, from one perspective, was remarkably inclusive for the period, embracing as many as two out of three white men, unlike Great Britain, where it was about one out of four. Still, since adult white males composed about twenty percent of the total population, somewhere between ten to sixteen percent of the population was eligible to vote in 1776.[25]

Several factors restricted voting, including laws in many colonies that based eligibility on property holding or the payment of taxes, on the theory that men who had property had a stake in society. Women could not vote because they had a different role in the hierarchy than men. In the Southern colonies, even free African Americans could not vote. In the eighteenth century, five colonies disfranchised Catholics, four disfranchised Jews. Slaves and Indians, comprising almost one-fifth of the population in 1790, also could not vote.[26]

In rural areas, it could be difficult just to get to the polls, and in many regions, of course, there was the powerful custom of "deference," in which the "common folk" deferred to the authority of their social and economic "betters."[27]

Ben Franklin poked fun at it all, especially the linkage between property holding and voting. A man, he pointed out, might own a jackass worth fifty dollars, which would entitle him to vote, but by the time the next election rolled around, the jackass, sad to say, had died. The man, meanwhile, had acquired more experience and could cast a wiser vote. Yet, with the jackass dead, he could not vote at all. "Now gentlemen, pray inform me," Franklin asked, "in whom is the right of suffrage? In the man or in the jackass?"[28]

Even as Franklin wrote, there were already powerful pressures for change. Washington Irving's famed Rip Van Winkle, who had the misfortune of sleeping through the Revolution, saw them firsthand. Returning to his village after his long nap, Rip found everything changed: his home, his neighbors, even his favorite inn where he had spent many happy hours. The old sign was still there, with "the ruby face" of King George, but it was different. "The red coat was changed for one of blue and buff, a sword was held in the hand instead of a scepter, the head was decorated with a cocked hat, and underneath was painted in large characters, GENERAL WASHINGTON."

Some things were still there, it was true, including the usual crowd of people drinking heartily outside the inn, but these were not his people; they were not drowsy or tranquil enough. They seemed pushy and argumentative instead; and worse, a "lean, bilious-looking fellow," his pockets full of handbills, suddenly rushed over and wanted, of all things, to know how Rip had voted.[29]

As old Rip discovered, in the twenty years he had been asleep a new sense of politics had swept the land. The time of the first party system had arrived, and elections and parties were undergoing important changes.

Politics had begun to touch those "bilious-looking" fellows, not just the elite. Ordinary Americans were beginning to experience the host of parades, festivals, civic feasts, badges, and songs that voiced their own participation in national politics.

Most Americans at the time celebrated George Washington, but if not him, then Independence Day. As Washington traveled for his first inauguration from Virginia to New York, huge crowds of people greeted him everywhere, showering him with reverence, triumphal arches, poetry, and music. A ceremonial barge carried him across the Hudson

River, to the sound of cannon and bands, and he long remembered the "joyful acclamations of every party and every description of citizens."[30]

*1833
Andrew Jackson
Medalet*

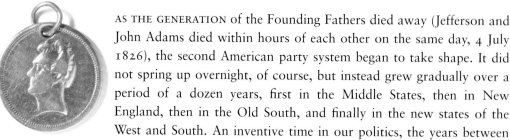

AS THE GENERATION of the Founding Fathers died away (Jefferson and John Adams died within hours of each other on the same day, 4 July 1826), the second American party system began to take shape. It did not spring up overnight, of course, but instead grew gradually over a period of a dozen years, first in the Middle States, then in New England, then in the Old South, and finally in the new states of the West and South. An inventive time in our politics, the years between the mid-1820s and 1860 saw the strengthening of political parties and the development of campaign techniques designed to persuade large numbers of men to vote. When the period ended, there was competition between two national political parties and a two-party system in every state.[31]

Americans, rather soon it turned out, had become used to the idea of having political parties. Unlike many of their forebears, they saw advantages in disciplined organizations that could conceive and enact programs, they liked the idea of a loyal opposition, and they came to value a party system that included regular competition between permanent party organizations.

Other changes reinforced their ideas. Thanks to new technologies, newspapers and magazines multiplied, transmitting political news more quickly and fully over a broader range of territory. Canals, steamboats, and railroads enlarged the political community, making it possible to hold state and national party conventions, put on rallies, conduct campaign tours, and extend politics into state and nation.[32]

As the number of elective offices on the state level grew, more people became involved in politics than ever before. To get them to vote, political parties turned to mass political mobilization. In state after state, legislatures eliminated property and other requirements for voting, settling instead on universal white manhood suffrage.[33]

Belonging to a political party, the era discovered, gave people a feeling of community, "an internalized sense of history, tradition, and common values." Once perceived as divisive, the parties became schools instead, teaching "seasonal courses in how to be Americans." Party activities became lessons in civics, their rituals visible everywhere, the language plain and understood, and they all affirmed democracy, mass participation, and the role of the "People" in the political process.[34]

This was all new, this "popular politics." Historians have called it "democratic theater," the way in which ordinary Americans took their place in the nation's politics. Torchlight parades, mass rallies, stump speeches, and election-day barbeques involved and empowered them. Emotion and display—the announcement of a person's partisan loyalties and his vote—made that vote more meaningful.

The politics of the street enabled voters and non-voters, men and women, parents and children, to take a visible part in the electoral process. All told, it was almost as revolutionary as the great Revolution that gave it life.[35]

Behind these developments lay important changes in the method of choosing presidential electors, changes that called for greater and greater voter participation in the election

ITEM 6
Andrew Jackson
"The Hero of
New Orleans"
glazed ceramic pitcher,
c. 1820.

of the president. In 1800 the legislatures in ten states chose presidential electors; voters chose them in only two. By 1824 that pattern had changed dramatically: legislatures chose electors in only six states, and after 1832 in only one.[36]

Election laws tried to tighten the relationship between voters and officeholders, an emphasis that filtered through the entire political system. They added a popular dimension to the race for president, increased the importance of state party machinery, weakened the influence of legislative caucuses, and brought about the use of national party conventions. Above all, they placed the quadrennial presidential election at the center of our politics.[37]

For various reasons the Democrats were the first to seize the changes, and between 1828 and 1832, they, under Andrew Jackson and Martin Van Buren, created the world's first mass political party. One could measure it in the turnout. People voted in 1828 and 1832 in more than double the proportion of the electorate that had voted in presidential elections ever before. Proportionally, in fact, Jackson's victory in 1832 drew a greater turnout than the election that first put Ronald Reagan into the White House.[38]

For our purposes, then, it is not surprising that the presidential campaigns of the period, especially the two Jackson campaigns of 1828 and 1832, saw the introduction of more and more campaign objects, such as tokens, buttons, pitchers and plates, bandanas, ribbons, flasks, combs, and thread boxes. Designed to stir the enthusiasm of all those new voters, they were among the first material objects ever used in campaigns.[39]

Jackson's backers waved hickory branches in honor of "Old Hickory." They used music, and were among the first to do so; they became the first (in Jackson's unsuccessful campaign of 1824) to issue a campaign biography. The first campaign buttons were issued in the 1824 campaign, struck by Jackson supporters, and holed at the top so they could be worn on a ribbon from the lapel. Jackson's 1832 re-election campaign witnessed the first torchlight parades. To appeal to women, the Jackson campaign of 1828 distributed sewing boxes and combs bearing pictures of Jackson.40

Jackson's victory in 1828—with fifty-six percent of the popular vote and an overwhelming margin in the Electoral College—displayed the success of the new methods and ensured their lasting effects. Thereafter, our presidential politics shifted more and more to party rivalries, intense party organizations, popular campaigning, and mass voter participation. Some critics complained that the new methods ignored issues and pandered to the ignorant masses—"Here is a revolution in the habits and manners of the people," John Quincy Adams spat out. "Where will it end?"—but they found it hard to argue against success. Before long, they or their parties had embraced the new methods.41

Other changes followed naturally in the wake.

Voter turnout rose sharply, from twenty-seven percent in 1824, to fifty-six percent in 1828, to seventy-eight percent in 1840. The parties also avidly pursued new voters, which resulted in a dramatic expansion of the suffrage.42

In 1833, Jackson became the first president to call himself the "direct representative" of the people and claim to have a mandate from the voters.43

There was a new spirit of party, in which individuals submerged their own desires in the larger interests of the cause. As a Tennessee congressman put it in 1836, "Union, harmony, self-denial, concession, everything for the cause, nothing for men, should be the watchword and motto of the Democratic party."44

Congressional caucuses once had nominated presidential candidates, but that method went by the wayside after 1824. Nomination by state legislatures did not work either, and in the 1830s, the parties settled on a national convention to ensure popular participation in the process.

In 1840, for the first time, the Democratic convention adopted a national platform, and eight years later it appointed the first national chairman and the first national committee. The fundamental apparatus was now in place to nominate candidates, organize campaigns, mobilize voters, and raise funds.45

Somewhere in heaven, Thomas Jefferson must have shuddered.

*1848
Lewis Cass
Medalet*

AND SHUDDERED AGAIN in 1840. That year, for the first time in our history, two parties that were organized on a national basis, the Whigs and the Democrats, fought for the presidency. In a remarkable development unforeseen by the country's leaders just a generation before, now both parties had competitive organizations in every state; both knew how to arouse popular enthusiasm. Remarkably, too, voters in every state had begun to think of themselves as either Whigs or Democrats, identifying with the symbols, personalities, and organizations of what they now viewed as *their* political party.46

By 1840, as one historian has noted, the parties were so well organized down to every ward and precinct, they were so good at bringing enormous numbers of voters to the polls, that "we may finally speak of the full emergence, in modern terms, of mass political parties, the first in the world."[47]

During the 1830s, a new party had taken form, united mainly by opposition to Jackson himself. Calling themselves the National Republicans and then, after 1834, the Whigs, they stole every element in the Democratic game: organization, pageantry, excitement, and imagery. In the hard-fought contest between the Democrats and the Whigs, the election of 1840 represented the maturation of the second party system.[48]

For a second term in the White House, the Democrats re-nominated Martin Van Buren, probably the era's most talented politician, the mastermind behind many of the recent party developments. The Whigs turned to a military hero who might rival Jackson in the popular imagination: General William Henry Harrison of Ohio, the victor in 1811 over Tecumseh, the great Shawnee chief, at the junction of the Tippecanoe and Wabash rivers. Balancing the ticket with John Tyler of Virginia, they came up with their famous slogan, "Tippecanoe and Tyler Too."[49]

The result was one of the best-known presidential campaigns in our history. The Whigs took the offensive from the start. Seizing on the new campaign techniques, they sent speakers into twenty-six states, including the famed Henry Clay and Daniel Webster. Harrison himself made two dozen speeches in Ohio, becoming the first presidential candidate to campaign on his own behalf. The Whigs organized mass meetings and rolled giant buckskin-covered balls bearing campaign slogans from city to city (the origin, by the way, of the phrase, "keep the ball rolling").[50]

One such ball, rolled by hand all the way from western Maryland to Baltimore, said,

> Farewell, dear Van
> You're not our man;
> To guide the ship
> We'll try Old Tip.[51]

Already ahead, the Whigs soon got an enormous break. Trying to persuade voters of Harrison's unfitness for the presidency, the *Baltimore Republican*, a Van Buren newspaper, suggested that a barrel of hard cider and a modest pension was all the Whig candidate needed, so he could "sit out the remainder of his days in his log cabin...and study moral philosophy."[52]

Whig editors seized on the image, and the Whigs, who had often borne the difficult label of the party of the rich, gathered in the cloak of the common man. Virtually overnight Harrison became the farmer and backwoodsman, comfortable in his log cabin, the same cabin he had left to fight for his country in the Indian wars and the War of 1812, a keg of hard cider by the door, the homey brew that formed his favorite drink.[53]

The image, of course, came nowhere close to matching reality. Harrison, as anyone who looked up the facts would know, was the son of Benjamin Harrison, a signer of the Declaration of Independence, and he grew up not in a log cabin but on a large Virginia plantation. As his own 1840 campaign began, he lived in a palatial mansion in Ohio, complete with white pillars, outbuildings, and an expansive lawn.[54]

ITEM 7
William Henry Harrison
Log Cabin textile,
1840 election.

Democrats countered with their own poetry:

Hush-a-bye-baby;
Daddy's a Whig,
Before he comes home
Hard cider he'll swig;
Then he'll be Tipsy
And over he'll fall;
Down will come Daddy,
Tip, Tyler and all.55

But it did little good. The Whigs, for this one year at least, had mastered the new techniques of popular and party involvement.

Above all, they had mastered the uses of the mass meeting, designed to excite voters and
get them to the polls. People turned out at Whig rallies in huge numbers, 50,000 or more.
"The people were here!" a Whig in Ohio exclaimed after one meeting, "hardy and indus-

trious yeomanry of the Buckeye soil," carrying banners and badges, listening to music "reverberating wildly through our highland hills and valleys...." At a rally in upstate New York, a party newspaper said, people "poured in from the Valleys and rushed in torrents down from the Mountains...vocal with Eloquence, with Music, and with Acclamations."[56]

Building on the earlier Jackson campaigns, Whig organizers used music. ("The spirit of song was everywhere," a young party member recalled, "and made the whole land vocal. The campaign was set to music....") They issued the first campaign songbook, containing tunes like "The Hard Cider Quick Step" and the "Log Cabin or Tippecanoe Waltz." Practicing inclusive politics, they found ways to bring women into the campaign, asking them to write pamphlets, give speeches, present toasts, cook campaign meals, and sew banners. "This way of making politicians of their women is something new under the sun," a Georgia Democrat complained, "but so it is the Whigs go to the strife."[57]

More than ever before, Whig leaders used Harrison's face in campaign literature and on campaign devices, giving him life to the voters. Buttons, banners, pitchers, and bandanas made him "The Log Cabin Candidate" and "The Ohio Farmer." He became both military hero and the symbol of rural virtues. "In Peace, the Farmer and his Ploughshare; In War, the Soldier and his Sword," one campaign ribbon said.[58]

A Philadelphia distiller, E. G. Booz, put his whisky into log cabin-shaped bottles, adding the word "booze" to our language.[59]

Van Buren, the master of the new politics, liked it not a bit, denouncing the Whig campaign as "a political Saturnalia."[60]

He liked it even less when he saw the election returns. More than four in every five eligible voters—80.2 percent, to be exact—turned out at the polls, compared to only 57.8 percent in 1836. Every state hit new peaks of participation; New York State had a turnout of 91.1 percent. William Henry Harrison won handily, 234 votes to 60 in the Electoral College.[61]

The defeated Democrats, who had pioneered most of the Whig techniques, had no sense of humor. They were so upset by the Log Cabin campaign that in 1844 they put a plank in their platform condemning "displays and appeals insulting to the judgment and subversive to the intellect of the people."[62]

★ III ★

AFTER THE 1830S, when state after state gave the vote to all white men regardless of birth or property, the United States had the most open electorate in the world, part of a larger sense of openness in economic and social life that restructured American society.

That electorate, to be sure, was limited to those who were male and those who were white, but it was a stunning development nonetheless that made the United States for much of the nineteenth century the only democracy in the world.[63]

But in mid-century it was a democracy that almost did not survive.

The second party system, so alive in the elections of the 1830s and 1840s, dissolved during the 1850s, in the midst of events no party system had ever witnessed before— or, thankfully, since. A major national party, the Whigs, simply disappeared; a new party rooted in a nativist, anti-Catholic secret society, the Know-Nothings, gained remarkable success; another new party, the Republicans, grounded in a sectional appeal against

ITEM 8
Wide-Awake Parade
engraving. Printed in
Harper's Weekly,
16 October 1860.

allowing slavery into the territories, rose to major-party status; and the Democrats, the dominant national party since the days of Jackson, disintegrated into an organization that fielded two candidates for president in 1860. And, finally, eleven states decided in 1861 to secede from the Union rather than accept the victory of Abraham Lincoln.[64]

These, of course, were among the most trying years in our history, a time of questioning about slavery and freedom, sectionalism, race relations, voting rights for women and others—about the continued existence of the Union itself.

Out of the troubles came the third or Civil War party system that would last from about the mid-1850s until the 1890s. A time of intense electoral competition, the third system was marked by new and larger polarities between North and South, greater attention to party management, new ideologies and style, and remarkably high voter turnout. It drew, in part, on a rise of anti-slavery, temperance, and anti-Catholic zeal.[65]

One of the key developments, of course, was the formation in 1854 of the Republican Party. In 1856 it named its first presidential candidate, the young and dashing John Charles Frémont. The Republicans hoped this famed western explorer known as "The Pathfinder" would attract a wide range of voters, just as Harrison had in 1840.

Successors to the Whigs, the Republicans from the start used the successful Whig tactics of 1840 to promote their candidate. Carrying imitation as far as they could, they even revived Harrison's log cabin symbol for Frémont—though it was no more appropriate for him than it had been for Harrison—and in a time of widening tensions over slavery and the territories, seized on the memorable slogan, "Free Speech, Free Press, Free Soil, Free Men, Frémont and Victory."[66]

They also sang, shouted, and marched. Calling themselves the "Wide-Awakes"—always awake against slavery—a marching group began in Hartford, Connecticut, in 1856, and spread quickly across the North, enrolling all told some 400,000 people. Members carried kerosene torches and wore glazed cloth capes to fend off the dripping oil; they marched in army formations. In a riveting display, row after row of marching men, torches burning, paraded through the darkened streets of towns and cities and passed before a reviewing stand on which the candidates for election stood. Tens of thousands of people watched and cheered.[67]

"You can hardly go out after dark without encountering a torchlight procession," a visitor to Maine wrote in 1860. "In the larger places not a night passes without a demonstration of some sort." The parades, as an Ohioan remarked, looked "like the waves of a river on fire." In some places women had their own Wide-Awake clubs, clad in cambric dresses, capes of the same material, and striped aprons of red, white, and blue, "each color bearing a single letter of the word 'Abe.'"[68]

Campaign buttons, banners, and badges reflected the serious issues the nation faced in 1860, especially slavery and disunion. Taking advantage of recent developments in the art of photography, button manufacturers for the first time produced ferrotype portraits of the candidates, encased in brass frames, a special benefit for Abraham Lincoln, whose features were not as well known as his rivals' for the White House.[69]

(It was a face, however, to remember. When Steven A. Douglas, his Illinois opponent, once accused Lincoln of being two-faced, Lincoln replied, "I leave it to my audience. If I had another face, do you think I'd wear this one?"[70])

In the heat of the campaign, Lincoln became "Honest Abe," "Old Abe"—a slogan we would never see in the youth-conscious culture of today—and, of course, "The Rail-Splitter," an image that not only harked back to the "Log Cabin" campaigns of Harrison and Frémont but also served to remind Lincoln, and those around him, of his ties to the working class.[71]

ITEM 9
Abraham Lincoln
"Rail Splitter"
brass medalet,
1860 election.

And, amazingly, in 1860, a scant half-dozen years after their party's founding, the Republicans won the presidency. Lincoln captured only two votes in every five, but with overwhelming margins across the North, he emerged the winner.

There was some thought he might lose in 1864—he himself was so sure of it that he drafted and signed a memorandum pledging to work with the new president-elect "to save the Union between the election and the inauguration..."—but timely victories on the part of the Union army saved him. The Democrats remained remarkably resilient, especially for a party identified with secession and war.[72]

The Democrats, in fact, came strikingly close to winning back the White House as early as 1868, just four years after the end of the war; and in 1874 they did win control of the House of Representatives, a control they maintained for all but four of the succeeding

ITEM 10
Embroidered
silk ribbons,
1868 & 1876
elections.

twenty years. In 1868 Horatio Seymour, the Democratic candidate, actually carried New York, New Jersey, and Oregon, a result, the shrewd Republican James G. Blaine noted with understatement, that "was not comforting" to the Republican leadership.[73]

With the war ended, the decades that followed became "the party period," the time of greatest attachment to political parties in our history. No wonder. Civil War loyalties, Republican or Democratic, often lasted a lifetime.

"We love our parties as we love our churches and our families," Senator Henry Blair of New Hampshire said in 1886. "We are part of them." "What the theatre is to the French, or the bull-fight or fandango to the Spanish, the hustings and the ballot-box are to *our* people," another observer said. "We are all politicians, men, women, and children."[74]

This seems strange language in the anti-party atmosphere of today, but in the late nineteenth century it rang true. Electoral politics in these years built on the deeper meanings they had acquired earlier in the century. Involving more than simply electing officials, they provided public recreation and entertainment and confirmed everyone's role in the democratic process. They linked the local with the national, as local campaigns fit into statewide results, which in turn determined the outcome in the nation at large.[75]

People actually "lived" their politics, which in the absence of national athletic events, was their era's spectator sport. They stood in the hot sun (or driving rain) and listened to speeches of three hours or more; they read party literature; they discussed the issues at home. Campaigns enlisted whole families, fathers, mothers, and children.

Party loyalty was handed down from fathers to sons, and to daughters as well. When a reporter from the *Springfield Republican* (Massachusetts) got home after casting his vote in the 1864 presidential election, he called his children into the garden and, as they watched, hung a Democratic ballot on a hook and set fire to it, while the children gave three cheers for "Old Abe." He wanted, the reporter said, to teach the children "their political duty in their youth."[76]

At election time, party workers—estimated at about five percent of the adult male population, the equivalent today, as one historian has noted, of all our golfers, tennis players, and skiers—put in ten or fifteen hours a week working for their party. More than half the population attended political speeches and rallies, as many as our summer visitors to zoos, fairs, amusement parks, and outdoor sports events put together. It was a very different time, indeed.[77]

THERE WERE THREE OTHER FEATURES that set politics apart in these years, the final decades of the third party system: elections were close, the franchise expanded, and people voted in extraordinary numbers.

*1884
Grover Cleveland
Pin*

In national elections, sixteen states, mostly in the North, consistently voted Republican; fourteen states, mostly in the South, consistently voted Democratic. Elections, therefore, depended on a handful of "doubtful" states, which could swing elections either way. These states—New York, New Jersey, Connecticut, Ohio, Indiana, and Illinois—received special attention at election time. Politicians lavished money and time on them; presidential candidates usually came from them. From 1868 to 1912, eight of the nine Republican presidential candidates and six of the seven Democratic candidates came from the "doubtful" states, especially New York and Ohio.

As a result, late nineteenth-century elections were close, the closest the country has ever experienced. In the five presidential elections between 1876 and 1892, an average differential of only 1.4 percent separated the Republican and Democratic candidates. The Republicans managed to win three of the five races, but they captured the majority of the popular vote in none of them, and they had a plurality only once, in 1880, and then it amounted to a scant 9,457 votes out of over 9.2 million cast. Republicans Rutherford B. Hayes and Benjamin Harrison won the presidency in 1876 and 1888 even though they actually trailed in the popular vote. Grover Cleveland's margin in 1884 over Blaine came to about twenty-nine thousand out of over ten million votes cast.[78]

Building on patterns that had started early in the century, the franchise again grew.

The adoption of the Fifteenth Amendment in 1870 gave the vote to most adult males, black as well as white—at least for a time. What was more, in twenty-two states, aliens could vote as well as citizens, and in much of the country, restrictions against office-holding diminished. Alabama, Missouri, Virginia, and Arkansas no longer required that their governors be born in the United States. New Hampshire, which had mandated that only Protestants could serve in state offices, dropped the provision in 1877, as did Massachusetts for its governor in 1892 and Delaware for its United States Senators in 1897.[79]

Finally, there was the amazing voter turnout, the highest voter mobilization in our history.

Large numbers of people, we should remember, remained unable to vote. Women could vote in national elections only in Wyoming and Utah, in Colorado (after 1893), and in

Idaho (after 1896). In recognition of their "natural" role, women could vote in school board elections in seventeen states, and in three states those with property could vote on measures involving taxes and bonds. African Americans, Asian Americans, and other minorities were also often kept from the polls.[80]

But among those who could vote, turnout was astonishingly high, averaging just under eighty percent of eligible voters in the presidential elections between 1868 and 1892, numbers unequalled before or since. In the presidential election of 1876, turnout nationwide reached 81.8 percent, the historic high for a presidential election. In only one presidential election—1872—did the turnout sink below seventy-five percent, and in 1896, almost eight voters in every ten went to the polls to vote for president.[81]

In parts of the North, the numbers could be dazzling. In Indiana, turnout averaged ninety-three percent in the presidential elections between 1868 and 1892; in New Jersey, eighty-nine percent. In the 1896 presidential election, more than ninety-five percent of the eligible voters cast ballots in the Midwest.[82]

To get these large turnouts, politicians in the period perfected the "army" or "military" style of campaigning, a new development in our long history of political campaigns. It must have seemed natural enough: they had lived, after all, through the massive battles of the Civil War, and they had hundreds of thousands of Civil War veterans who could not wait to march.[83]

Elections, in this new "military" style, became battles, the two parties formed armies, voters were troops, and the polls were the battlefield. "Even the language of politics," as one historian has noted, "was cast in military terms." At the *opening gun* of the *campaign*, the *standard bearer*, along with his fellow *war-horses*, *rallied* the *rank and file* around the party *standard*. Precinct *captains* set their *phalanxes* to *mobilize* voters; party *headquarters* used their *war chest* to *enlist* supporters; party literature *armed* men for *battle*; and, on Election Day, the *well-drilled* ranks overwhelmed the opponent's *camp* and claimed the *spoils* of victory.[84]

The "military" style lasted roughly through the late 1880s, though remnants of it could be seen many years later. Since virtually everyone belonged to one party (army) or the other, the party's task was not so much to convert voters as to get them out on Election Day. To do that, it employed badges, uniforms, parades, and mass gatherings to listen to party speakers. Fireworks and cannon fire simulated the battlefield.[85]

Torchlight parades were the key to it all. Young Herbert Hoover never forgot the first torchlight parade he ever saw. It was 1880, and he was six years old. "I was not only allowed out that night, but I saw the torches being filled and lighted," he recalled years later. "I was not high enough to carry one but I was permitted to walk alongside the parade."[86]

The parades were huge. When James G. Blaine came to Indianapolis to stump for Benjamin Harrison in 1888, there were 25,000 marchers, forty brass bands, and dozens of flag-laden floats; it took an hour and a half for the marchers to pass the reviewing stand, and something on the order of 100,000 people looked on. On 1 November 1896, well after the "military" style had begun to wane, over 100,000 people marched for Republican candidate William McKinley in a "Sound Money" parade down Broadway in New York City.[87]

Before long, however, the tactics began to change.

The change started in the late 1880s and early 1890s, when important elements in the electorate became more independent-minded, less prone to respond to the emotional

THE LIFE OF
JAMES G. BLAINE.

For President--JAMES G. BLAINE.
For Vice-President--JOHN A. LOGAN.

ITEM 11
James G. Blaine
& John A. Logan
Campaign Biography,
1884.

"military" style. Sensing this, political leaders soon shifted their strategy to appeal more and more to voters through publicity, advertising, and reasoned discussion. A new style of campaign, the "merchandizing" or "educational" style, was born.

It still aimed, of course, at turning out voters, but it placed more emphasis on winning new supporters with thoughtful argument. It looked, therefore, to pamphlets and advertising, and it exploited smaller meetings with as few as several hundred people who listened to expert speakers unravel the mysteries of the major issues of the day.[88]

Mass meetings and bonfires began to disappear, and so did the torchlight parades. Wisconsin Republicans concluded in 1892 that "they can put campaign funds to better uses than the purchase of uniforms, torches and banners, the hiring of brass bands and all the rest. They consider that not many votes are made in that way." In a telling moment, an Indiana reporter in 1916 happened to come across an old kerosene torch, left over from the 1892 campaign, and wondered why in heaven's name people had ever carried them in parades. All they did, he wrote, was to drip oil on the marchers' clothes.[89]

A torchlight parade, the *New York Times* remarked even more caustically in 1924, could work only in an era of drab farm or village life. "There are no villages now," the *Times* said smugly. "We are all urban, children of the movie and the radio, speeders of the car, 'fed up' with searchlights and colored lights."[90]

(The Republicans purchased the last torches in 1900, ending a marvelous half-century tradition that had stirred many a voter.[91])

The "educational" style came to a peak in the exciting 1896 campaign that pitted McKinley against William Jennings Bryan, the candidate of the Democratic and People's parties. Bryan, as we know, took his campaign on the road, aware that his rebellious candidacy lacked the usual support of party newspapers and party organizations. Contrary to legend, he was far from the first to do so. William Henry Harrison had campaigned in 1840, Steven A. Douglas in 1860, Horatio Seymour in 1868, Horace Greeley in 1872, and James G. Blaine in 1884.[92]

But he *was* the first presidential candidate to make a *systematic* tour of the states he needed for election. In a display of remarkable stamina, he traveled more than 29,000 miles and delivered 570 speeches in twenty-nine states, speaking to audiences totaling two or three million people. "It used to be the newspapers educated the people," he said to a rally in Des Moines, Iowa, "but now the people educate the newspapers."[93]

McKinley adopted the same strategy in a different way. His headquarters in Chicago had a large educational organization designed to create and distribute new kinds of campaign materials. It included a Literary Bureau, a Speakers' Bureau, and departments that looked after the needs of specific groups, such as unions, African Americans, Germans, Scandinavians, college students, and traveling salesmen.

The Literary Bureau, into which the McKinley campaign poured a great deal of money, prepared material for Republican newspapers across the country; giving voters something to read, it produced over 200 different pamphlets, printed in twenty-one languages, on the gold standard, the tariff, and other issues. The mailing room had 100 full-time employees who sent out, all told, more than 100 million documents. "The operation," as one historian has noted, "has never been rivaled in American politics."[94]

And that was not all. McKinley himself conducted a "front porch campaign," modeled on the stay-at-home campaigns of Garfield in 1880 and Benjamin Harrison in 1888. ("I have great risk of meeting a fool at home," Harrison had said at the time, "but the candidate who travels cannot escape him."[95]) Trains carried as many as 750,000 persons to his home, a figure that amounted to about five percent of the total vote and thirteen percent of the entire Republican vote that fall. There he greeted them with freshly prepared remarks, ready for printing in Republican newspapers across the country. All together, McKinley gave three hundred speeches, all from his front porch.[96]

"This is a year for press and pen," he remarked. "The sword has been sheathed. The only force now needed is the force of reason and the only power to be invoked is that of intelligence and patriotism."[97]

THERE WAS ONE OTHER FORCE that year, evident in this exhibition. A revolution in political campaigning occurred in 1896—the arrival of the celluloid pin-back button, which, once produced, spread more rapidly than any other single item in the history of our politics. In the 1896 campaign alone, more than a thousand varieties of celluloids publicized the presidential candidates. They were cheap, often less than a penny apiece, durable, and attachable to clothing. Able to display any artwork that could be printed on a paper disk, they made possible an array of designs and colors that the metal badges of an earlier era could not carry.[98]

*1896
McKinley/Hobart
Button*

Highly visible, the new buttons could convey a wide range of candidate and party messages. Wearing one on the shirt or lapel, voters could declare their political preferences for all to see.[99]

McKinley buttons often featured his likeness, along with slogans such as "The Advance Agent of Prosperity" and a "Full Dinner Pail," both promising a return to prosperity after the devastating depression of the 1890s. Bryan materials usually related to the silver issue, making his campaign the most sharply focused since Frémont's in 1856. Whether for McKinley or Bryan, buttons and images proliferated. Experts have counted at least two thousand types of items for the 1896 campaign, virtually double the number produced in any previous presidential election.[100]

EVERYTHING WORKED, at least in drawing out the voters. In the election of 1896, nearly eighty percent of eligible voters across the nation cast ballots; in some states, turnouts ran far higher than that.

*1896
William Jennings Bryan
Silver Bug*

It all seemed well and good. Who could argue, after all, against campaigns that stressed education and reasoned argument? But for our political parties and our political system there was a penalty, at first unrecognized, to the "educational" style—an erosion of partisan loyalty that over decades would result in a drastic drop in voter turnout. Politics stirred and involved fewer voters, emphasized the personalities of candidates, and in the absence of mass involvement, promoted the participation of pressure groups.[101]

In some sense, the result was unfortunate. Something important was lost: a feeling of involvement, a point of vital contact between voter and system, an assurance that democratic politics could work.[102]

★ IV ★

THE REMARKABLE THEODORE ROOSEVELT did his best to restore it, making governance a matter of personal responsibility. TR, as he himself was quick to note, brought important changes to the presidency and to presidential politics, including a focus on his own personality—to the point, as someone once said, that at a wedding he wanted to be the bride, at a funeral the corpse. Henry Adams, overwhelmed with TR's restless energy, called him "pure act." "You must always remember," a British friend remarked in 1904, "that the President is about six."[103]

"Taft is a far abler man than I," TR once wrote of his ill-starred successor, "but he don't know how to play the popular hero and shoot a bear."[104]

In his several campaigns for office, Roosevelt somehow brought together most of the images of the presidential past: the war hero of Washington, Jackson, the first Harrison, and Grant; the common touch of Abraham Lincoln; the frontier image of Frémont and Jackson; the intellectual ability of Thomas Jefferson. He was easy to portray. Campaign objects, as the items in this exhibition show, often depicted his teeth—"almost as big as colt's teeth," a New York newspaper once said—his work on his Dakota ranch, or his experience as a Rough Rider during the Spanish-American War.[105]

While TR was transforming the presidency into the famed "bully pulpit," developments beyond his control were changing presidential politics.

During the late 1890s, the third party system began to give way to the fourth, a time when interest in politics fell sharply. Fewer people took the trouble to vote. In the last five presidential elections of the nineteenth century, turnout averaged 79.2 percent; in the first five presidential elections of the new century, it averaged only 65 percent, a dramatic drop. Owing to measures in the South designed to take away the vote from blacks and poor whites, the fall-off was most severe there, but it occurred in every area of the country.

"The drop in voting," one historian has noted, "was nationwide, substantial, and cumulative." It also had never occurred before, neither in our own history—for more than a hundred years we had broadened suffrage and boosted turnout—nor in what was going on in other Western democracies.[106]

And it was enduring. Turnout rates, to be sure, fluctuated during the twentieth century—dropping in the 1920s, rising somewhat in the 1930s, stabilizing after World War II, and then falling again after 1960—but they remained fairly close to the levels seen before World War I.[107]

Why did it happen?

For one thing, the massive Republican realignment of the 1890s, inaugurating more than three decades of Republican dominance, reduced partisan competition in most parts of the country. With minor exceptions, Republicans took charge in the North, Midwest, and West, and Democrats in the South. In many areas party competition dwindled, which reduced voter enthusiasm, which in turn reduced turnout.[108]

Nationwide, the Republicans went on to victory after victory, losing in 1912 to Woodrow Wilson only because of the split in their own ranks—between TR, who ran as an insurgent on the Progressive party ticket, and William Howard Taft. The Democrats bumbled, confined to their Southern stronghold and voters in some Northern cities. In 1924 the Democratic National Convention took an embarrassing 103 ballots to choose its presidential nominee, and party members wondered what had happened to the great party of Andrew Jackson. As Will Rogers put it, "I am not a member of any organized political party—I am a Democrat."[109]

The adoption of the Australian secret ballot, which spread rapidly across the country during the 1880s and 1890s, also dampened party spirit. The secret ballot, of course, represented an important advance in cleaning up politics, but at the same time it weakened the political party. No longer could parties print their own ballots, which allowed cheating and encouraged people to vote a straight ticket; no longer could party workers at the polls

THIS BALLOT SHOULD BE MARKED IN ONE OF TWO WAYS WITH A PENCIL HAVING BLACK LEAD.
TO VOTE A STRAIGHT TICKET, MAKE A CROSS X MARK WITHIN THE CIRCLE ABOVE ONE OF THE PARTY COLUMNS.
TO VOTE A SPLIT TICKET, THAT IS FOR CANDIDATES OF DIFFERENT PARTIES, THE VOTER SHOULD MAKE A CROSS X MARK BEFORE THE NAME OF EACH CANDIDATE FOR WHOM HE VOTES.
IF THE TICKET MARKED IN THE CIRCLE FOR A STRAIGHT TICKET DOES NOT CONTAIN THE NAMES OF CANDIDATES FOR ALL OFFICES FOR WHICH THE ELECTOR MAY VOTE, HE MAY VOTE FOR CANDIDATES FOR SUCH OFFICES SO OMITTED BY MAKING A CROSS X MARK BEFORE THE NAMES OF CANDIDATES FOR SUCH OFFICES ON ANOTHER TICKET, OR, BY WRITING THE NAMES, IF THEY ARE NOT PRINTED UPON THE BALLOT, IN THE BLANK COLUMN UNDER THE TITLE OF THE OFFICE.
TO VOTE FOR A PERSON NOT ON THE BALLOT, WRITE THE NAME OF SUCH PERSON, UNDER THE TITLE OF THE OFFICE, IN THE BLANK COLUMN.
ANY OTHER MARK THAN THE CROSS X MARK USED FOR THE PURPOSE OF VOTING, OR ANY ERASURE MADE ON THIS BALLOT, MAKES IT VOID, AND NO VOTE CAN BE COUNTED HEREON.
IF YOU TEAR, OR DEFACE, OR WRONGLY MARK THIS BALLOT, RETURN IT AND OBTAIN ANOTHER.

(Perforation)

REPUBLICAN TICKET.	DEMOCRATIC TICKET.	NATIONAL DEMOCRATIC TICKET.	PROHIBITION TICKET.	SOCIALIST LABOR TICKET.	PEOPLE'S TICKET.	BLANK COLUMN.
For President, WILLIAM McKINLEY.	For President, WILLIAM J. BRYAN.	For President, JOHN M. PALMER.	For President, JOSHUA LEVERING.	For President, CHARLES H. MATCHETT.	For President, WILLIAM J. BRYAN.	THE ELECTOR MAY WRITE IN THE COLUMN BELOW, UNDER THE TITLE OF THE OFFICE, THE NAME OF ANY PERSON WHOSE NAME IS NOT PRINTED UPON THE BALLOT, FOR WHOM HE DESIRES TO VOTE.
For Vice-President, GARRET A. HOBART.	For Vice-President, ARTHUR SEWALL.	For Vice-President, SIMON B. BUCKNER.	For Vice-President, HALE JOHNSON.	For Vice-President, MATTHEW MAGUIRE.	For Vice-President, THOMAS E. WATSON.	
For Electors of President and Vice-President, BENJAMIN F. TRACY	For Electors of President and Vice-President, ROBERT P. BUSH.	For Electors of President and Vice-President, OSWALD OTTENDORFER.	For Electors of President and Vice-President, FREDERICK F. WHEELER.	For Electors of President and Vice-President, GEORGE ABELSON.	For Electors of President and Vice-President, ROBERT P. BUSH.	For Electors of President and Vice-President,
EDWARD H. BUTLER.	BENJAMIN WOOD.	THEODORE BACON.	LOUIS ALBERT BANKS.	THOMAS J. MURPHY.	BENJAMIN WOOD.	
CARLL S. BURR.	JOHN P. MADDAN.	PATRICK J. GLEASON.	HENRY W. RANDALL.	ABRAHAM SHAPIRA.	JOHN P. MADDEN.	
ALEXANDER ROSS.	ANDREW McLEAN.	GEORGE W. WINGATE.	FREEBORN G. SMITH.	CARL WENDELSTEIN.	ANDREW McLEAN.	
CHARLES A. MOORE.	JAMES BURRELL.	JAMES A. MURTHA, Jr.	JAMES MEYER.	OTTO HATJE.	JAMES BURRELL.	
ROBERT A. SHARKEY.	SAMUEL A. WHITEHOUSE.	HENRY W. SHERRILL.	FRANK MAPES.	WALFRID A. OSSBORG.	SAMUEL S. WHITEHOUSE.	
Here follow 30 other names.	Here follow 30 other names.	Here follow 30 other names.	Here follow 30 other names.	Here follow 30 other names.	Here follow 30 other names.	
For Governor, FRANK S. BLACK.	For Governor, WILBUR F. PORTER.	For Governor, DANIEL G. GRIFFIN.	For Governor, WILLIAM W. SMITH.	For Governor, HOWARD BALKAM.	For Governor, WILBUR F. PORTER.	For Governor,
For Lieutenant Governor, TIMOTHY L. WOODRUFF.	For Lieutenant Governor, FREDERICK C. SCHRAUB.	For Lieutenant Governor, FREDERICK W. HINRICHS.	For Lieutenant Governor, CHARLES E. LATIMER.	For Lieutenant Governor, FREDERICK BENNETS.	For Lieutenant Governor, FRED C. SCHRAUB.	For Lieutenant Governor,
For Associate Judge of the Court of Appeals, IRVING G. VANN.	For Associate Judge of the Court of Appeals, ROBERT U. TITUS.	For Associate Judge of the Court of Appeals, SPENCER CLINTON.	For Associate Judge of the Court of Appeals, ELIAS ROOT.	For Associate Judge of the Court of Appeals, THEODORE F. CUNO.	For Associate Judge of the Court of Appeals, LAWRENCE J. McPARLIN.	For Associate Judge of the Court of Appeals,
For Justice of Supreme Court, FRANK H. HISCOCK.	For Justice of Supreme Court, JOHN W. SHEA.	For Justice of Supreme Court, NO NOMINATION.	For Justice of Supreme Court, NO NOMINATION.	For Justice of Supreme Court, NO NOMINATION.	For Justice of Supreme Court, NO NOMINATION.	For Justice of Supreme Court,
For Representative in Congress, CHARLES A. CHICKERING.	For Representative in Congress, OSCAR M. WOOD.	For Representative in Congress, OSCAR M. WOOD.	For Representative in Congress, FREDERICK E. DEVENDORF.	For Representative in Congress, NO NOMINATION.	For Representative in Congress, NO NOMINATION.	For Representative in Congress,
For Member of Assembly, WALTER ZIMMERMAN.	For Member of Assembly, FRANCIS T. WATSON.	For Member of Assembly, CARL W. HAAS.	For Member of Assembly, ALONZO M. LEFFINGWELL.	For Member of Assembly, NO NOMINATION.	For Member of Assembly, NO NOMINATION.	For Member of Assembly,
For Sheriff, SAMUEL R. KELLOGG.	For Sheriff, JAMES ELDRIDGE GREEN.	For Sheriff, JAMES ELDRIDGE GREEN.	For Sheriff, GEORGE W. HERRICK.	For Sheriff, NO NOMINATION.	For Sheriff, NO NOMINATION.	For Sheriff,
For County Treasurer, FRANKLIN M. PARKER.	For County Treasurer, WILLIAM M. PENNIMAN.	For County Treasurer, WILLIAM M. PENNIMAN.	For County Treasurer, OLNEY W. HART.	For County Treasurer, NO NOMINATION.	For County Treasurer, NO NOMINATION.	For County Treasurer,
For School Commissioner, R. SHERIDAN CLARK.	For School Commissioner, ELTON R. COON.	For School Commissioner, L GIDEON EKLSEY.	For School Commissioner, C. JAY SARGENT.	For School Commissioner, NO NOMINATION.	For School Commissioner, NO NOMINATION.	For School Commissioner,

ITEM 12
New York presidential ballot, 1896 election.

watch how people voted. The secret ballot, in short, worked well for political honesty, but not so well for voter turnout.[110]

In the first two decades of the twentieth century, a time of massive immigration from abroad, a number of states narrowed the franchise by adopting literacy tests for voters, and some raised the length of their residency requirements. More and more states required voters to register personally, shifting the responsibility for registration from the state to the individual, and eliminating those voters who failed to register on time or at all.[111]

Women's suffrage, adopted nationwide in 1920, played an ironic role in depressing turnout figures: it swelled the size of the eligible electorate, but women for years voted in smaller proportions than men. Voting rates among blacks in the South plummeted, reflecting the intent of Southern whites to keep them from the polls. By 1908, all of the eleven former Confederate states required payment of a poll tax in order to vote, and seven of them also had literacy requirements. The combination of both on Southern voting was devastating.[112]

Finally, during the fourth party system, people consciously worked to weaken the power of politicians and parties through measures such as direct primaries, direct election of United States Senators, and the initiative, referendum, and recall—all designed to bring voters more directly into the process. At the same time, Americans turned more and more to their professional associations, not their parties, to get things done. Lawyers, doctors, and teachers formed professional societies; farmers joined co-operatives; businessmen banded together in trade associations.[113]

The old array of campaign activities—parades, rallies, and bonfires—diminished. Campaign buttons were still produced, but were worn rarely. Campaign managers relied on media and advertising rather than on the older forms of mass voter mobilization. A growing range of leisure-time activities, such as professional baseball, amusement parks, vaudeville, and circuses, diverted Americans from politics in new ways. Political campaigns, once one of the occasions around which Americans organized their lives, became listless and dull.[114]

1920
Warren G. Harding
Button

IN AN ATTEMPT TO CHANGE THAT, Warren G. Harding in 1920 conducted something of a front-porch campaign, reminiscent of those of Garfield, Benjamin Harrison, and McKinley. Party leaders, in fact, had hoped he would stay at home. "If he goes out on the hustings," one of them said, "he's the sort of damned fool who will try to answer questions."[115]

But the strategy had another purpose, too, calculated to evoke the old, simple, small-town America in a nation that was rushing to cities and factories. To make sure no one missed the connection, party workers brought the flagpole from McKinley's front yard and erected it on Harding's. Al Jolson sang his campaign song, "Harding, You're the Man for Us," which included the line, "We need another Lincoln to do the nation's thinkin'." Harding himself played the tuba. It was one of the first alliances between presidential politics and the nation's growing entertainment industry, so prominent later on in the era of Ronald Reagan and Bill Clinton.[116]

The appeal to the past fooled no one. There were too many signs of the new America, some of them evident in the Harding campaign itself.

One was political advertising. Advertising executives had first entered presidential politics in a substantial way in the elections of 1912 and 1916. Recognizing that the charms of the "Full Dinner Pail" had worked for McKinley in 1896, they came up with an appealing campaign for Woodrow Wilson in 1916, highlighted by the slogan "He Kept Us Out of War." Large posters showed a nation at peace, factories running at full blast, and a happy worker coming home to a smiling wife and two children, all below a picture of Wilson. At the bottom it said, "He Has Protected Me and Mine."[117]

Albert Lasker, one of the most renowned of the era's advertising experts, took charge of the Harding campaign, though the slogan he came up with—"Let's be done with wiggle and wobble"—left something to be desired. Still, he "sold" Harding on billboards and in magazines, "positioning" him as an old-fashioned, honest, Midwesterner.[118]

He sold him, too, on radio, an even more important landmark of the new America. Radio, and of course television in later years, transformed political campaigns forever. Messages moved almost instantly across the country. Image, personality, and sound bytes became more and more vital. Experts began to learn how to "stage manage"—a telling phrase—political personalities and use modern marketing tools to persuade voters and win elections.

ITEM 13
Warren G. Harding
& Calvin Coolidge
beanie, 1920 election.

Radio had its first significant outing on 2 November 1920, when station KDKA in Pittsburgh broadcast for the first time the results of a presidential election. Harding, the winner, became the first president to be heard on radio, but Calvin Coolidge, his successor, actually used it with greater effectiveness, an interesting fact given Coolidge's reputation for stubborn silence. (Informed that Coolidge was dead, Dorothy Parker, the famous wit, replied, "How can you tell?") During his time in office, more people heard Coolidge's voice than had heard all of his predecessors combined.[119]

In 1923 he delivered his State of the Union address over the radio, the first president to do so, and he tapped radio's help during his 1924 campaign for election. ("During the campaign he had little to say and said it well," William Allan White, the famous Kansas journalist, said of Coolidge that year.) On 4 March 1925, twenty-one radio stations across the country carried his inaugural address, to perhaps fifteen million listeners. Those in awe of the new and the modern shivered as they heard him turn the pages.

In another breakthrough, radio broadcast the national party conventions for the first time in 1924. Helpful to the Republicans, it was unfortunate for the Democrats, whose convention staggered through 103 ballots. It also showed its early power to shape reputations. One of the period's most famous speakers, William Jennings Bryan, "the Boy Orator of the Platte," turned out to have a poor voice for radio, while Franklin D. Roosevelt began his brilliant radio career with his eloquent nomination of fellow New Yorker, the "Happy Warrior," Alfred E. Smith, for the presidency.[120]

1932
Franklin D. Roosevelt
Button

ROOSEVELT, IN FACT, became the key figure in a new party system, the fifth, that grew out of the elections of 1928 and 1932. Elections in this system were hard-fought, and they clearly reflected social divisions within our society, exposed, for example, in the bitter 1928 campaign between Yankee Protestant Herbert Hoover and Irish Catholic Al Smith.

Voters for the moment pinned the blame for the Great Depression on the Republican party. The Democrats won election after election, becoming the country's majority party for the first time since the early 1850s, nearly a hundred years before.

They did something more. Under Franklin D. Roosevelt and the New Deal, they restructured the political system—indeed, the whole society—around the power and money of the federal government. In ways never seen before, New Deal programs affected voters' lives every day. The Civil Works Administration, the Works Progress Administration, and other relief agencies gave jobs to over seven million adults; the National Youth Administration did the same for several million young people, most of whom never forgot it. The Homeowners' Loan Association helped refinance one of every five private mortgages; the Social Security Act established a system of old-age insurance for virtually everyone; the Tennessee Valley Authority and the Rural Electrification Administration introduced electric power into millions of rural homes.

All together, FDR and the New Deal reshaped the ways Americans thought, acted, and voted.

In the crisis of the Depression, FDR appealed for a time to virtually everyone. Using the radio as no president had used it before, he gave in his first two years in office six "Fireside Chats," talking to millions of Americans—"my friends," he called them warmly—in ways that convinced them he knew about their problems. Among many, he inspired enormous affection, even veneration, reminiscent to some degree of George Washington. "My mother looks upon the President as someone so immediately concerned with her problems and difficulties," one man said in the 1930s, "that she would not be greatly surprised were he to come to her house some evening and stay to dinner."[121]

Yet the Roosevelt coalition turned out to be too broad, unable to satisfy the expectations of everyone in it. Large numbers of voters who disagreed with FDR on social and economic issues had voted for him out of disappointment with Herbert Hoover and the Republicans. When economic recovery did not come immediately, many of them shifted back to the Republican column.[122]

Still, FDR's legacy endured, in politics as well as ongoing government programs. To his party's traditional stronghold in the South, he had added urban voters, immigrants, labor, Catholics, minorities, women, and the poor, a new political coalition—the famous and powerful New Deal coalition—parts of which have lasted until the present day.[123]

Behind the scenes, however, new forces were at work to reshape our politics. A nation of abundance and suburbs, gleaming automobiles and glowing television sets, America yearned to put the feelings of the Depression and war behind it, and there was a political party ready to do just that. It was the Republican Party, and they were about to put together a winning coalition of their own.

IT STARTED, according to some accounts, in 1947 during halftime at a Texas high school football game, when the Abilene High School band used flash cards and a marching formation to try to lure a famous army general to run for the presidency. While the appeal did not work for another five years, "I like Ike" became one of the most successful political slogans in American history.[124]

And Ike himself, as it turned out, became the first candidate (and president) to exploit television, a medium that despite his awkwardness he used with skill.

As with radio, TV cameras had made their first appearance at the Republican and Democratic conventions in 1940, when NBC and Philco televised parts of both conventions to an audience of about 50,000 people who lived near the transmitter on the Empire State Building in New York City. In 1948 television networks extended their coverage to about ten million people, most of them still living in the Northeast, and by 1952 carried the conventions to a national audience. In 1968 they broadcast them for the first time in color.[125]

The parties, as they so often have throughout our history, adjusted quickly to the new medium. As early as 1948 they arranged their convention agendas to deal with routine matters during the day and important business in the viewer-rich evening. That year, too, television began to manipulate images to entertain its audience. Learning of the plan of some Southern delegates to walk out of the Democratic convention over the civil rights plank in the platform, a director persuaded them to march first to the NBC studios at the end of the hall and rip off their convention badges in front of the cameras.[126]

That was dramatic, but audiences and markets were small—in 1948 fewer than three percent of the population owned a television set—and so were the ideas about how to use this new medium. When President Harry S Truman taped one of the first "spot" announcements ever aired that year, it offered no political message and simply encouraged people to vote.[127]

Then Eisenhower and his advisors began to work the revolution. By 1952 there were some 18 million television sets in the country, and viewers were eager to follow the conventions and campaign. About forty percent of all families—more than fifty percent of all voters—tuned into the national conventions, a figure that would be the envy of the parties today.[128]

Watching the conventions was so popular, in fact, that advertisers actually built ad campaigns around them, something the Whigs in 1840, with all their inventive flair, might have done, too. "Buy a television, watch the conventions," RCA urged. "With the aid of television," another RCA ad said, "we had what amounted to the greatest town meeting ever held.... Sixty million people had front-row seats and got a better picture of what was going on than any delegate or any reporter on the convention floor."[129]

(Over time, fewer and fewer people took those fabled front-row seats, and the great town meeting, sadly, shrank. In 1952 the average television household watched twenty-five hours of convention coverage. In 1996 it watched four hours; in 2000, three hours. Only thirteen percent of television households even had their sets turned on for the most recent national conventions.[130])

In 1952 the Eisenhower campaign became the first to hire an advertising agency full-time. Rosser Reeves, a top executive with the Ted Bates agency in New York, produced the first "spot" commercials, aimed at an audience he was sure, as a long-time marketer of business products, had a limited attention span. That meant "spots" of thirty seconds, certainly no more than a minute. "I think of a man in a voting booth who hesitates between two levers as if he were pausing between competing tubes of toothpaste in a drugstore...," Reeves said. "The brand that has made the highest penetration in his brain will win his choice..."[131]

To get that kind of penetration, Eisenhower's admen ran a program, "Eisenhower Answers America," in which people on the street asked the candidate questions. To find the people, Reeves rounded up tourists who were waiting in line to see the show at New York's Radio City Music Hall and took them to a studio where he filmed their questions for the candidate.

"WOMAN: You know what things cost today. High prices are just driving me crazy."

"EISENHOWER: Yes, my Mamie gets after me about the high cost of living. It's another reason why I say it's time for a change. Time to get back to an honest dollar and an honest dollar's work."

Or:

"WOMAN: The Democrats have made mistakes, but aren't their intentions good?"

"EISENHOWER: Well, if the driver of your school bus runs into a truck, hits a lamppost, drives into a ditch, you don't say his intentions are good. You get a new bus driver."[132]

Once, between takes, Eisenhower shook his head and muttered sadly, "To think that an old soldier should come to this."[133]

Occurring so soon after the advent of television, Ike's 1952 campaign saw another first, the pre-emption of favorite television programs for political ads. Most people did not like it, especially when Republican managers even pre-empted the nation's top-rated program—everyone's favorite—I Love Lucy. Telegrams flooded the network, many of them bearing a clear message, "I like Ike. But I Love Lucy."[134]

It was expensive—their media campaign cost the Republicans close to $1.5 million (the Democrats spent only $77,000)—but effective.[135]

Adlai Stevenson, the Illinois governor and intellectual who was Eisenhower's Democratic opponent, was aghast. "The idea," he said, "that you can merchandize candidates for high office like breakfast cereal, and that you can gather votes like boxtops, is, I think, the ultimate indignity for the Democratic process." After losing, Stevenson had the added thought that it might have been better if the parties had simply purchased a half-hour of radio and TV silence, "during which the audience would be asked to think quietly for themselves."[136]

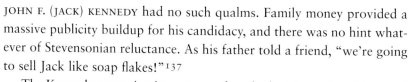

1961
John F. Kennedy
Medal

JOHN F. (JACK) KENNEDY had no such qualms. Family money provided a massive publicity buildup for his candidacy, and there was no hint whatever of Stevensonian reluctance. As his father told a friend, "we're going to sell Jack like soap flakes!"[137]

The Kennedy campaign in 1960 employed television, advertising, and polling data more than any campaign before, using professional pollsters to test voter sentiment on different issues (a relatively new concept) and nail down wins in key primaries.[138]

Kennedy also "won" the opening televised debate—or so said polls of viewers—the first between presidential candidates in our history. The Kennedy-Nixon debates have long since entered political legend. Seventy-five million people watched the first one, a remarkable total, and sixty-three million the last. During all four debates, the TV audience never fell below fifty percent of the nation's adult population.[139]

(Those figures meant that about sixty percent of all households with television sets watched the four debates. By 1984 Reagan-Mondale attracted only forty-six percent; in 1988, Bush-Dukakis about thirty-six percent; in 1996, Clinton-Dole just twenty-nine percent. In 2000, the Bush-Gore debates attracted overall about the same percentage of viewers, but the third debate drew only twenty-six percent, the worst ever.[140])

With Kennedy's victory in mind, presidential candidates after 1960 increasingly embraced television as the way to communicate with voters. They cut back on the number of paid party workers and relied on television and television advertising to get their message to the electorate. Professional campaign managers and media consultants played greater and greater roles in campaigns.[141]

Campaign ads and news began to merge in viewers' minds, a phenomenon that experts call "meltdown." As Robert Mulholland, a former president of NBC, has noted: "Some of the ads start to look like news stories; they're the same length, 30 seconds.... Television is not just separated in the minds of the viewer between this is news, this is commercial, and this is entertainment. Sometimes it all gets fuzzed up because it all comes into the home through the same little piece of glass."[142]

"American politics and television are now so completely locked together," Theodore White, the renowned political observer, has noted, "that it is impossible to tell the story of the one without the other."[143]

No wonder. Studies show that Americans spend more time watching television than any activity other than sleeping or working. Seven of ten Americans, it is true, read a daily newspaper and two of ten read a weekly magazine; there are twice as many radios as there are people. But ninety-nine percent of households have television sets (more than half, in fact, have two or more), which are turned on an average of six hours and forty-four minutes a day. In the year 2000, fifty-seven percent of Americans called television their main source of information for world events.[144]

Television news shapes politics in a variety of ways. It tends, for one thing, to focus on the personalities of candidates and on the race for the presidency; congressional, gubernatorial, and other races are largely ignored. To sharpen the drama, it often names an early front-runner, the candidate most likely to win, who becomes on the small screen the central figure of the campaign. Victory is his if he can overcome the obstacles between himself and the White House. It then selects his leading opponent and covers his challenge to the front-runner, thus narrowing the field to two candidates and harming the chances of all the rest.[145]

To complete the picture, TV journalists, in a remarkable reversal of earlier eras, get more "news time" than the presidential candidates themselves. In campaigns during the late 1990s, the candidates received about one-sixth as much speaking time as the reporters who covered them; they became brief sound bytes. In 1968, the average candidate sound byte was 42.3 seconds; in 1996 it was 7.2 seconds.[146]

To put the thought another way, for every minute that George Bush and Al Gore were heard on the evening newscasts in 2000, the journalists covering them were heard for six minutes. Bush's single appearance on CBS's *The Late Show with David Letterman* in mid-October gave him almost as much airtime as he had on all of *CBS Evening News* during the entire campaign.[147]

Television has had another, more hidden, effect on our presidential politics—the attention given to vice presidents as future candidates for the presidency. When the Republicans in 1960 chose Richard Nixon as their presidential candidate, it was the first time in more than a century that a vice president had been selected to replace a retiring incumbent (the last one was Martin Van Buren in 1836). Since then, of course, vice presidents have won the nomination again and again, in part because television has expanded their visibility and given them important advantages over their rivals.[148]

*1968
Richard M. Nixon
Button*

NIXON, IN SOME WAYS, inaugurated the new and most recent era in our politics, the growing strength of the Republican party and the powerful role of conservatives within it.

Following the strategy of political author Kevin Phillips, whose 1969 book *The Emerging Republican Majority* was widely read, Nixon worked during his first term to combine his party's traditional constituency with the growing number of voters who questioned the Civil Rights, anti-war, and social reform movements of the late 1960s. Many of these voters had tended to support the Democrats in the past, including white Southerners, blue-collar workers, and followers of conservative religions.[149]

Nixon's triumph became clear in 1972, when he carried forty-nine states and won by nearly eighteen million votes, the largest margin in our history. His opponent, George McGovern, was cast as an out-of-date liberal, a throwback to a discredited time. Reflecting new Republican strengths, Nixon swept the South, receiving over seventy percent of the vote in some Southern states, the first candidate to carry all eleven states of the old Confederacy since FDR had in 1944.[150]

Nixon stumbled badly, of course, and Watergate forever tarnished his presidency and his legacy.

Nixon's time in office even affected exhibitions like this one. After Watergate, the 1974 Federal Election Campaign Act limited campaign contributions and expenditures, and allocations for buttons and other campaign items dropped dramatically. In August 1976, the commission created under the act ruled that party committees could spend no more than $1,000 in promoting presidential nominees.

Since then, national party organizations have wound up spending so much money on media, travel, and other costs that little has remained for the traditional buttons and bumper stickers. Campaigns have cut back on distributing items to voters. In 1976 Jimmy Carter's media director made the decision not to distribute campaign buttons at all, but when local Carter-Mondale workers complained bitterly, he agreed to buy 200,000 cheap tin buttons, about one for every volunteer, saying, "Who wears buttons? It's the people who work in the headquarters operations. If you send them enough for themselves, they'll have them and that's that."[151]

Despite Nixon's errors, later politicians would continue to build on his new Republican majority.

A variety of issues, from the Equal Rights Amendment to abortion, gave them fresh momentum in the 1970s and 1980s. Many Catholics, who had voted Democratic for more than a century, joined religious Republicans in opposition to abortion. Influential Democrats, thinking their party had become too liberal, organized a "neo-conservative" movement that had great influence on the Republican party. Republicans began to adopt the tax reduction philosophy that marks the party to this day.

Leading it all was Ronald Wilson Reagan, actor, television performer, and governor of California, who took advantage of the nation's swing toward conservatism. Some veteran Republicans took Reagan too lightly—Nixon called him "a lightweight and not someone to be considered seriously"—and later rued their mistake. In line with the voters' mood, he believed fervently in states' rights and limited government, in reduced taxes, and in greater spending on defense. The federal government, he announced in November 1975, in his first run for the presidency, "has become more intrusive, more coercive, more meddlesome and less effective."[152]

In 1980 he played skillfully on the woes of the Carter administration, including economic troubles at home and weaknesses abroad. "A recession," he said during the campaign, "is when your neighbor loses his job. A depression is when you lose *your* job. And recovery will be when Jimmy Carter loses *his*." Carter, of course, did lose, and with the help of the "Moral Majority," a conservative religious movement led by Rev. Jerry Falwell, the Republicans for the first time in nearly thirty years captured control of the Senate.[153]

During his first term, Reagan kept his eye on three major goals—a reduction of taxes, an increase in spending for defense, and a loosening of government regulations in many areas of American life—and, remarkably, he accomplished them all. Running for re-election in 1984, he celebrated "Morning in America," his television ads featuring small town barbershops, the Statue of Liberty, patriotic parades, scenes of rural tranquility, and Americans on the job.

It all worked. Reagan brought together the Sunbelt and suburbs, many old New Dealers, the religious right, and others into an enormous victory. He carried forty-nine of fifty states and fell just a few votes short in the fiftieth. (Walter Mondale, his opponent, carried his own state of Minnesota by only 3,761 votes out of 2,680,906 cast.) He took 58.8 percent of the popular vote, the fifth highest total in the twentieth century, and won a record 525 electoral votes, surpassing Roosevelt's 523 electoral votes in 1936.[154]

Thanks to Iran-Contra and other problems, Reagan's reputation suffered during his second term, and the Republicans lost control of the Senate in 1986. But Reagan did complete two terms, the first president to do that since Eisenhower, and he restored a welcome sense of self-confidence to the nation.

He also became the uncontested hero of the modern Republican party. The new Republicans of the 1980s and 1990s disdained Lincoln for his staunch defense of the federal government and his views on race; disliked TR's penchant for social reform and greater government power; considered Eisenhower's brand of Republicanism a surrender to the liberals; and scorned Nixon for Watergate. Reagan's policies of smaller government, tax cuts, deregulation, and increased defense spending had become the central tenets of Republican orthodoxy.[155]

Stay with those tenets, the new Republicans believed, and they could look forward to a generation of control over the White House and Congress.

IT DIDN'T WORK OUT that way. George H. W. Bush, Reagan's designated heir, stumbled in the presidency, especially on the tax issue in 1990, when he went back on his popular slogan, "Read my lips. No new taxes." People read his lips and in 1992 voted the other way. They also turned away from Newt Gingrich's "Contract with America." Seizing on a conservative agenda—"It is impossible," Gingrich said, "to maintain civilization with twelve-year-olds having babies, fifteen-year-olds killing each other; seventeen-year-olds dying of AIDS, and eighteen-year-olds receiving diplomas they cannot read"—the Republicans had managed to take control of the House of Representatives in 1994, for the first time in forty years, but after a sad display of political and personal weaknesses, they lost their way.[156]

The 1992 presidential campaign offered some intriguing incidents: candidate Bill Clinton saying he did not inhale; a voter asking President Bush what the national debt meant to him personally; Ross Perot withdrawing from the campaign because Republican plotters were going to disrupt his daughter's wedding; Vice President Dan Quayle misspelling the word "potato"; Admiral James Stockdale, the vice-presidential candidate on the Perot ticket, asking in the midst of the vice-presidential debate, "Who am I? What am I doing here?"[157]

Clinton won, but he captured a majority of the popular vote only in his home state of Arkansas. When he won again in 1996, it was the first time since FDR in 1936, sixty years before, that a Democratic president had been re-elected for a second full term in the White House. Forty-nine percent of the eligible voters cast ballots for president that year.[158]

In 1998's congressional elections it was thirty-six percent, and, remarkably, more than half the children in the country lived in a household where neither parent voted.

In campaign 2000, the networks cut back their coverage of the national conventions, the settings that had once been the centerpiece of those great town meetings of 1952. NBC and Fox also decided not even to broadcast ninety minutes of the first debate between Bush and Gore: NBC televised a baseball game, Fox its regular prime time programming. The number of people watching the debates sank to the lowest level ever, some forty million fewer than watched the first Kennedy-Nixon debate in 1960.

Barely fifty-one percent of eligible voters went to the polls in 2000, which meant that only about twenty-five percent of the electorate—about one in four—voted for either Bush or Gore. In seven states—one of them, interestingly enough, George Bush's home state of Texas—more votes were cast in a gubernatorial or Senate race than were cast for president.[159]

In 2000, 105.4 million people went to the polls; 100.4 million did not.[160]

There were important consequences of that: if all eligible voters had cast their ballots in 2000, polls showed, the Democrats would have won the presidency and both houses of Congress.[161]

ITEM 14
Reform Party poster,
1992 election.

The election results again suggested growing divisions in the country. Al Gore won more female, black, urban, union, and non-gun-owning voters, more new immigrants or recent descendants of immigrants, more non-church-going families, and more pro-choice women. George Bush, on the other hand, won more white men, especially in the South, more gun owners, more men and women opposed to abortion, more people who lived in the country, and more religious conservatives.

"We have two massive, colliding forces," the *Washington Post* said. "One is rural, Christian, religiously conservative with guns at home, terribly unhappy with Clinton's behavior.... And we have a second America that is socially tolerant, pro-choice, secular, living in New England and the Pacific coast, and in the affluent suburbs."[162]

★ V ★

THAT BRINGS US TO THE PRESENT DAY.

We are now, it is clear, working our way toward a fresh understanding of our politics and our political culture, in ways sometimes so fundamental that we might be reminded of the questions the Founding Fathers posed at the beginning of this exhibition.

In some respects the news is good.

While we vote at rates much lower than other democratic nations—twenty to thirty percentage points below voters in Europe, for example—we take part in the actual workings of government, through contacts with public officials and other means, at rates substantially above Europeans. We write more letters to our congressional representatives than we ever have before. We join political organizations of various kinds—special interest groups, community organizations, and political action committees—in large numbers, both locally and nationally.[163]

We are the only country that chooses the lower house of the national legislature as often as every two years. We are virtually unique in the broad range of offices—judges, sheriffs, city councils, county officials, and attorneys general, to name a few—that are elective positions. Our elections, we should remember, fill over 500,000 offices in the United States within each four-year political cycle, an astounding number, about one to every one hundred families.[164]

We continue, as we have through much of our history, to add voters to the rolls. The "Motor Voter" bill, which took effect on 1 January 1995, added in less than two years about nine million voters to the electorate, not all of whom, of course, voted. As the twenty-first century gets underway, nearly all adult citizens are legally entitled to vote.[165]

Finally, some states have found that "same-day" registration, which allows citizens to register even on Election Day, increases turnout dramatically. In the six states that have that law, turnout in 2000 was fifteen percentage points higher than in other states. Minnesota, one of them, leads the nation in turnout rate, including a remarkable rate of sixty-nine percent in 2000. Adopted nationwide, experts think, "same-day" registration would increase voter turnout by five percent.[166]

2000
Albert Gore, Jr.
Button

STILL, WE MUST FACE THE FACT that our turnout has slumped badly, so badly that we now rank among the lowest of all democracies in the world, twenty-third, in fact, among twenty-four democratic nations.[167]

(Interestingly, those who do not vote seem to feel some shame. In virtually every presidential election since the 1980s, a good many more people reported that they voted than actually had.[168])

The patterns are pretty clear. Whites, people between the ages of forty-five and sixty-five, non-Southerners, people with higher family incomes, people with higher levels of education, white-collar workers, and professionals tend to vote more. Minorities, the poor, the young, the less educated, and those in lower-status occupations tend to vote less.[169]

In 1994, 60 percent of eligible Americans with incomes greater than $50,000 a year went to the polls; among those who earned under $5,000 a year, only 19.9 percent did.[170]

As figures like these suggest, the overall decline in voting has given more power proportionally to those who *do* vote, including people who are older, who earn more, or who hold strong opinions on issues like gun control and abortion.

Some commentators—among them the well-known conservative columnist George Will of the *Washington Post*—point with satisfaction to the low turnout, arguing that if apathetic voters stay home, it is better for the country.[171]

Others are more worried, especially about the young, the generation that will oversee our democracy during the coming decades.

Remember that in the mid-1800s youngsters coming of voting age voted in enormous numbers, as many as eight out of every ten. In 1971, passage of the Twenty-Sixth Amendment, enfranchising people between the ages of eighteen and twenty, added about twenty-five million potential voters to the rolls. The Amendment's supporters had confidently predicted large turnouts, but they were wrong. Among adults under the age of thirty, only thirty percent voted in 2000.[172]

It was not for lack of trying. MTV ran a "Choose or Lose" campaign aimed at young voters, with a slogan saying, "You might as well pull the lever, What 'chu afraid of?" Groups like Rock the Vote placed voter registration tables at rock concerts around the country, aired public-service announcements on widely-watched MTV, and established a toll-free 800 number to tell voters how to register. Madonna served as a Rock the Vote announcer, appearing in a red bikini, black motorcycle boots, and an American flag. Flanked by two young men, she urged viewers to vote—or get a spanking.

It might have been interesting to see what people chose, but then it was learned that Madonna herself was not registered to vote.[173]

Young or old, people have turned increasingly to politically active interest groups, believing them more effective in attaining their goals than the traditional political parties.

In an important move, Congress in 1974 changed the campaign finance law to recognize Political Action Committees. Within a decade, PACs had increased in number from 600 to 4,000. Corporations make up more than forty-five percent of all Congressional pressure groups; women, who comprise more than half the population, have about one percent of them. There are no PACs looking after the interests of migrant laborers, child-care workers, or a host of other people.[174]

About two-thirds of us, some recent polls have shown, think that interest groups run our government.[175]

New methods have changed the way our politics work. We select our presidential candidates more and more through primaries, which unroll, in presidential years, in relentless succession. Some major states, especially in the South, have grouped their primaries on a single date, making "Super Tuesday" increasingly important in determining the final nominees. Yet voters have lost confidence in the primary system and say they would prefer almost any alternative, including a return to old-style political conventions.[176]

Computers complete tasks that once had been the treasured job of a ward or precinct leader. They put together demographic studies, churn out voting statistics, and evaluate the results of opinion polls; they print literature, address mail, and keep financial reports. Professional polling organizations test voter views, often using focus groups, another new technique, to try out campaign issues.

Direct mail, loading our mailboxes, has brought about a new form of grass roots involvement in politics. Richard Viguerie, the best-known figure in the field, started his direct-mail corporation in 1965 with $400 and the membership list of the conservative group, Young Americans for Freedom. A decade later, he had on computer tapes more than thirty million names of conservative-leaning people, employed 300 persons, and mailed each year seventy-six million letters. All of them predicted disastrous defeat for conservative causes—unless, of course, the recipient sent money.[177]

Thomas Jefferson still shudders in heaven.

1956
Stevenson/Kefauver
Pin

BUT SHOULD HE? "From George to George" has been a remarkable story—and, we trust, an informative exhibition. Parties and PACs, torches and television—a great deal has happened in the 250 years of our history that is traversed in these rooms. The objects here show a spirit akin to Jefferson's own: experimental, adventuresome, hopeful for democracy, adjusting again and again to changing conditions in a changing country. Jefferson himself, after all, completed the daring Louisiana Purchase two centuries ago.

Will Rogers once remarked that "Presidential elections are a good deal like marriages. There is no accounting for one's taste."[178] But there *is* an accounting for the people's tastes, the many ways in which they have affirmed the gift of a democratic society, and it lies in the display cases around you.

ENDNOTES

1. Robert Dallek, *Hail to the Chief: The Making and Unmaking of American Presidents* (New York: Hyperion, 1996), p. xii.

2. Robert H. Wiebe, *Self-Rule: A Cultural History of American Democracy* (Chicago: University of Chicago Press, 1995), p. 1.

3. Wiebe, *Self-Rule*, p. 10.

4. Charles Dickens, *American Notes* (Bloomsbury, England: The Nonesuch Press, 1938), p. 60.

5. Mark Lawrence Kornbluh, *Why America Stopped Voting: The Decline of Participatory Democracy and the Emergence of Modern American Politics* (New York: New York University Press, 2000), pp. 23-25.

6. Morton Keller, *Affairs of State: Public Life in Late Nineteenth Century America* (Cambridge, Mass.: Harvard University Press, 1977), p. 241.

7. Alexis de Tocqueville, *Democracy in America*, 2 vols. (New York: Everyman's Library, Alfred A. Knopf, 1994), 1:249.

8. Angus Campbell, Philip E. Converse, Warren E. Miller, and Donald E. Stokes, *The American Voter* (New York: John Wiley and Sons, 1960), p. 3.

9. Jack C. Doppelt and Ellen Shearer, *Nonvoters: America's No-Shows* (Thousand Oaks, Calif.: Sage Publications, 1999), pp. 5-6; Thomas E. Patterson, *The Vanishing Voter: Public Involvement in an Age of Uncertainty* (New York: Alfred A. Knopf, 2002), p. 10.

10. Paul Kleppner, *Who Voted? The Dynamics of Electoral Turnout, 1870-1980* (New York: Praeger, 1982), pp. 19-20.

11. Patterson, *Vanishing Voter*, p. 10.

12. Patterson, *Vanishing Voter*, p. 4.

13. Patterson, *Vanishing Voter*, pp. 4-5.

14. Campbell, Converse, Miller, and Stokes, *American Voter*, pp. 531-35.

15. Campbell, Converse, Miller, and Stokes, *American Voter*, pp. 531-81; Walter Dean Burnham, "The United States: The Politics of Heterogeneity," in Richard Rose, ed., *Electoral Behavior: A Comparative Handbook* (New York: Free Press, 1974), pp. 664-69; Gerald M. Pomper with Susan S. Lederman, *Elections in America: Control and Influence in Democratic Politics*, 2nd ed. (New York: Longman, 1980), pp. 99-125; Robert D. DiClerico, *Political Parties, Campaigns, and Elections* (Upper Saddle River, N.J.: Prentice Hall, 2000), p. 191.

16. Everett Carll Ladd, "1996 Vote: The 'No Majority' Realignment Continues," and Alan I. Abramowitz and Kyle L. Saunders, "Ideological Realignment in the U.S. Electorate," both in DiClerico, *Political Parties, Campaigns, and Elections*, pp. 199-212, 214-28.

17. Kornbluh, *Why America Stopped Voting*, p. 6; V. O. Key, Jr., "A Theory of Critical Elections," *Journal of Politics* 17 (Feb. 1955): 3-18; V.O. Key, Jr., "Secular Realignments and the Party System," *Journal of Politics* 21 (May 1959): 198-210; Walter Dean Burnham, *Critical Elections and the Mainsprings of American Politics* (New York: W.W. Norton and Company, 1970); William G. Shade, "Elections, Parties, and the Stages of American Political Development," in L. Sandy Maisel and William G. Shade, *Parties and Politics in American History: A Reader* (New York: Garland Publishing, Inc., 1994), pp. 1-22; Michael McGerr, *The Decline of Popular Politics: The American North, 1865-1928* (New York: Oxford University Press, 1986), p. 7.

18. Paul Kleppner, *The Third Electoral System, 1853-1892: Parties, Voters, and Political Cultures* (Chapel Hill, N.C.: University of North Carolina Press, 1979), p. 19.

19. Kleppner, *Third Electoral System*, pp. 19-47; Burnham, *Critical Elections and the Mainsprings of American Politics*, p. 11; McGerr, *Decline of Popular Politics*, pp. 7-8.

20. George A. Peek, Jr., *The Political Writings of John Adams* (Indianapolis, Ind.: Bobbs-Merrill, 1954), p. 146; James A. Morone, *The Democratic Wish: Popular Participation and the Limits of American Government* (New York: Basic Books, 1990), p. 33; Mark E. Kann, *The Gendering of American Politics: Founding Mothers, Founding Fathers, and Political Patriarchy* (Westport, Conn.: Praeger, 1999), pp. 71, 91; Mark E. Kann, *A Republic of Men: The American Founders, Gendered Language, and Patriarchal Politics* (New York: New York University Press, 1998), p. 1.

21. Patricia U. Bonomi, ed., *Party and Political Opposition in Revolutionary America* (Tarrytown, N.Y.: Sleepy Hollow Press, 1980), pp. ix, 101-102; Ralph Ketcham, *Presidents Above Party: The First American Presidency, 1789-1829* (Chapel Hill, NC: University of North Carolina Press, 1984), pp. 89-123; Thomas S. Langston, *With Reverence and Contempt: How Americans Think About Their President* (Baltimore, Md.: Johns Hopkins University Press, 1995), p. 68.

22. Arthur M. Schlesinger, Jr., "Introduction," *History of U.S. Political Parties*, 4 vols. (New York: Chelsea House Publishers, 1973), 1:xxxiv; G. Scott Thomas, *The Pursuit of the White House: A Handbook of Presidential Election Statistics and History* (Westport, Conn.: Greenwood Press, 1987), p. 3.

23. George Washington, "Farewell Address," Sept. 19, 1796, in John Rhodehamel, ed. *George Washington: Writings* (New York: Library of America, 1997), pp. 969-70.

24. George Dargo, "Parties and the Transformation of the Constitutional Idea in Revolutionary Pennsylvania," in Bonomi, *Party and Political Opposition in Revolutionary America*, pp. 111-12; Alexander Keyssar, *The Right to Vote: The Contested History of Democracy in the United States* (New York: Basic Books, 2000), p. 4.

25. Christopher Collier, "The American People as Christian White Men of Property," in Donald W. Rogers, ed., *Voting and the Spirit of American Democracy: Essays on the History of Voting and Voting Rights in America* (Urbana, Ill.: University of Illinois Press 1992), p. 24; Wiebe, *Self-Rule*, p. 30; Donald W. Rogers, "Introduction: The Right to Vote in American History," in Rogers, *Voting and the Spirit of American Democracy*, p. 6.

26. Keyssar, *Right to Vote*, pp. 5-6; *Presidential Elections since 1789* (Washington, D.C.: Congressional Quarterly, Inc., 1987), p. 88; Chilton Williamson, *American Suffrage: From Property to Democracy, 1760-1860* (Princeton, N.J.: Princeton University Press, 1960), pp. 12-19.

27. Rogers, "Introduction," in Rogers, *Voting and the Spirit of American Democracy*, p. 7; M. J. Heale, *The Making of American Politics, 1750-1850* (New York: Longman, 1977), p. 105. As for actual voters, turnout ran as high as about forty percent in Virginia down to ten percent in Massachusetts and Connecticut: Collier, "The American People as Christian White Men of Property" in Rogers, *Voting and the Spirit of American Democracy*, pp. 20-21.

28. Benjamin Franklin as quoted in Keyssar, *Right to Vote*, p. 3.

29. Washington Irving, *Rip Van Winkle: A Legend of the Kaatskill Mountains* (New York: G.P. Putnam and Sons, 1870), pp. 22-23.

30. Simon T. Newman, *Parades and the Politics of the Street: Festive Culture in the Early American Republic* (Philadelphia: University of Pennsylvania Press, 1997), pp. xiii, 1-10, 83-151; Douglas Southall Freeman, *George Washington: A Biography*, Volume Six: *Patriot and President* (New York: Charles Scribner's Sons, 1954), pp. 167-84; James Thomas Flexner, *George Washington and the New Nation, 1783-1793* (Boston: Little, Brown, and Company, 1970), pp. 174-88.

31. Richard P. McCormick, *The Second American Party System: Party Formation in the Jacksonian Era* (Chapel Hill, N.C.: University of North Carolina Press, 1966), pp. 3-6, 14; Keith Melder, *Hail to the Candidate: Presidential Campaigns from Banners to Broadcasts* (Washington, D.C.: The Smithsonian Institute, 1992), p. 69; M. J. Heale, *The Presidential Quest: Candidates and Images in American Political Culture, 1787-1852* (New York: Longman, 1982), p. 151.

32. McCormick, *Second American Party System*, p. 30.

33. Sean Wilentz, "Property and Power: Suffrage Reform in the United States, 1787-1860," in Rogers, *Voting and the Spirit of American Democracy,* p. 31; Richard P. McCormick, *The Presidential Game: The Origins of American Presidential Politics* (New York: Oxford University Press, 1982), p. 154.

34. Joel H. Silbey, *Political Ideology and Voting Behavior in the Age of Jackson* (Inglewood Cliffs, N.J.: Prentice-Hall, Inc., 1974), p. 216; Jean H. Baker, "The Ceremonies of Politics: Nineteenth-Century Rituals of National Affirmation," in William J. Cooper, Jr., Michael F. Holt, and John McCardell, eds., *A Master's Due: Essays in Honor of David Herbert Donald* (Baton Rouge, La.: Louisiana State University Press, 1985), pp. 168-75; Michael McGerr, "Political Style and Women's Power, 1830-1930," *Journal of American History* 77 (Dec. 1990): 865.

35. McGerr, *Decline of Popular Politics*, pp. 5-6.

36. McCormick, *Second American Party System*, pp. 28-29. The remaining state was South Carolina.

37. McCormick, *Second American Party System*, p. 29.

38. Langston, *With Reverence and Contempt*, p. 79; Melder, *Hail to the Candidate,* p. 70; Heale, *Presidential Quest*, p. vii.

39. Roger A. Fischer, *Tippecanoe and Trinkets Too: The Material Culture of Presidential Campaigns, 1828-1984* (Urbana, Ill.: University of Illinois Press, 1988), pp. 1, 9-21; Melder, *Hail to the Candidate,* p. 24; J. Doyle DeWitt, *A Century of Campaign Buttons 1789-1889* (Hartford, Conn.: The Traveler's Press, 1959), p. 13; Edmund B. Sullivan, *American Political Badges and Medalets, 1789-1892* (Lawrence, Mass.: Quarterman Publications, Inc., 1981), p. 19.

40. Joanne Morreale, *The Presidential Campaign Film: A Critical History* (Westport, Conn.: Praeger, 1993), pp. 28-29; Melder, *Hail to the Candidate,* p. 28; Kathleen Hall Jamieson, *Packaging the Presidency: A History and Criticism of Presidential Campaign Advertising* (New York: Oxford University Press, 1984), p. 6; DeWitt, *Century of Campaign Buttons,* p. i.

41. Entry of Aug. 29, 1840, in Charles Francis Adams, ed., *Memoirs of John Quincy Adams, Comprising Portions of His Diary from 1795 to 1848,* 12 vols. (Philadelphia: J.B. Lippincott & Co., 1874-1877), 10:352.

42. Keyssar, *Right to Vote,* p. 40.

43. Langston, *With Reverence and Contempt*, p. 69.

44. Joel H. Silbey, "Election of 1836," in Schlesinger, *History of American Presidential Elections,* 1:585.

45. Schlesinger, "Introduction," *History of American Presidential Elections,* 1:xli-xlii.

46. McCormick, *Second American Party System*, p. 342.

47. Robert Kelley, "Ideology and Political Culture from Jefferson to Nixon," *American Historical Review* 82 (June 1977): 541.

48. Heale, *Making of American Politics*, p. 184.

49. William Nisbet Chambers, "Election of 1840," in Schlesinger, *History of American Presidential Elections,* 1:658-59.

50. Chambers, "Election of 1840," in Schlesinger, *History of American Presidential Elections,* 1:643-90; Jamieson, *Packaging the Presidency,* pp. 12-13; Robert Gray Gunderson, *The Log-Cabin Campaign* (Westport, Conn.: Greenwood Press, 1957), pp. 165-72; Fischer, *Tippecanoe and Trinkets Too,* p. 31.

51. Gunderson, *Log-Cabin Campaign,* p. 4.

52. Gunderson, *Log-Cabin Campaign,* pp. 74-75.

53. Gunderson, *Log-Cabin Campaign,* pp. 123-47.

54. Jamieson, *Packaging the Presidency,* pp. 9-11; Morreale, *Presidential Campaign Film,* p. 29.

55. Chambers, "Election of 1840," in Schlesinger, *History of American Presidential Elections,* 1:672.

56. A. Banning Norton, *The Great Revolution of 1840: Reminiscences of the Log Cabin and Hard Cider Campaign* (Mt. Vernon, Ohio, and Dallas, Tex.: A.B. Norton and Co., 1888), p. 215; *The Log Cabin,* Aug. 22, 1840, in Melder, *Hail to the Candidate,* p. 79.

57. George Washington Julian, *Political Recollections: 1840-1872* (Chicago: Jansen, McClurg, and Co., 1884), p. 17; Jamieson, *Packaging the Presidency,* p. 9; Fischer, *Tippecanoe and Trinkets Too,* p. 30; Gunderson, *Log-Cabin Campaign,* pp. 135, 137-39.

58. Fischer, *Tippecanoe and Trinkets Too,* pp. 41-45; Roger A. Fischer and Edmund B. Sullivan, *American Political Ribbons and Ribbon Badges, 1825-1981* (Lincoln, Mass.: Quarterman Publications, Inc., 1985), p. 6.

59. Chambers, "Election of 1840," in Schlesinger, *History of American Presidential Elections,* 1:670.

60. Fischer, *Tippecanoe and Trinkets Too,* p. 29.

61. Chambers, "Election of 1840," in Schlesinger, *History of American Presidential Elections,* 1:680-81; Melder, *Hail to the Candidate,* p. 89; McCormick, *Second American Party System,* pp. 341-42.

62. DeWitt, *Century of Campaign Buttons,* p. 65.

63. R. Hal Williams, "The Politics of the Gilded Age," in John F. Marszalek and Wilson D. Miscamble, eds., *American Political History: Essays on the State of the Discipline* (Notre Dame, Ind.: University of Notre Dame Press, 1997), p. 110.

64. Paul J. Kleppner, *The Third Electoral System, 1853-1892: Parties, Voters, and Political Cultures* (Chapel Hill, N.C.: University of North Carolina Press, 1979), pp. 48-49.

65. Kleppner, *Third Electoral System,* pp. 28-29, 70, 142; Williams, "Politics of the Gilded Age," p. 111.

66. Fischer, *Tippecanoe and Trinkets Too,* pp. 71-72.

67. Osborne H. Oldroyd, *Lincoln's Campaign: or, The Political Revolution of 1860* (Chicago: Laird and Lee, 1896), pp. 104-109; Edmund B. Sullivan, *Collecting Political Americana* (New York: Crown Publishers, Inc., 1980), pp. 144-46; McGerr, *Decline of Popular Politics,* p. 24.

68. McGerr, *Decline of Popular Politics,* p. 28; *Springfield Republican* (MA), Oct. 15, 1860.

69. DeWitt, *Century of Campaign Buttons,* pp. i, 126; Sullivan, *American Political Badges and Medalets,* p. vii.

70. Kathleen Hall Jamieson, *Dirty Politics: Deception, Distraction, and Democracy* (New York: Oxford University Press, 1992), p. 46.

71. Fischer, *Tippecanoe and Trinkets Too,* pp. 83-85; Fischer and Sullivan, *American Political Ribbons and Ribbon Badges,* p. 104.

72. David Herbert Donald, *Lincoln* (New York: Simon and Schuster, 1995), p. 529.

73. James Gillespie Blaine, *Twenty Years of Congress: From Lincoln to Garfield, with a Review of the Events which Led to the Political Revolution of 1860,* 2 vols. (Norwich, Conn.: The Henry Bill Publishing Company, 1884–1886), 2:408. As Blaine pointed out, if Seymour had carried the South, which was then occupied by federal troops, he would have actually won the election, an amazing thought so close to the end of the Civil War.

74. Williams, "Politics of the Gilded Age," p. 108.

75. Kornbluh, *Why America Stopped Voting,* pp. 29-31.

76. Dale Baum, *The Civil War Party System: The Case of Massachusetts, 1848-1876* (Chapel Hill, N.C.: University of North Carolina Press, 1984), p. 8.

77. Richard J. Jensen, *Grassroots Politics: Parties, Issues, and Voters, 1854-1983* (Westport, Conn.: Greenwood Press, 1983), p. 31.

78. For an excellent brief summary of Gilded Age elections, see Samuel T. McSeveney, *The Politics of Depression: Political Behavior in the Northeast, 1893-1896* (New York: Oxford University Press, 1972), pp. 3-31; U.S. Bureau of Census, "Electoral and Popular Vote Cast for President, By Political Party: 1789-1968," in *Historical Statistics of the United States from Colonial Times to 1970*, Bicentennial Edition (Washington, D.C.: U.S. Department of Commerce, Bureau of Census, 1975), 2:1073; Peter F. Nardulli, "A Normal Vote Approach to Electoral Change: Presidential Elections, 1828-1984," *Political Behavior* 16 (Dec. 1994): 483-84.

79. Robert J. Steinfeld, "Property and Suffrage in the Early American Republic," *Stanford Law Review* 41 (Jan. 1989): 335-76; Williamson, *American Suffrage*; Keller, *Affairs of State*, pp. 522–23.

80. Keller, *Affairs of State*, p. 442; Paula Baker, "The Domestication of Politics: Women and American Political Society, 1780–1920," *American Historical Review* 89 (June 1984): 634n.

81. Rogers, "Introduction," in Rogers, *Voting and the Spirit of American Democracy*, p. 11. In a significant—and disturbing—contrast to today's trends, the young, those just coming of voting age in the mid-1890s, had a turnout rate of 79.6 percent, a measure of the strong forces leading people to vote: Kleppner, *Who Voted?*, p. 48.

82. U.S. Bureau of the Census, "Voter Participation in Presidential Elections by State: 1824 to 1968," in *Historical Statistics of the United States*, 2:1071–72; Walter Dean Burnham, "Those High Nineteenth-Century American Voting Turnouts: Fact or Fiction?" *Journal of Interdisciplinary History* 16 (Spring 1985): 613–44; Burnham, *Critical Elections and the Mainsprings of American Politics*, pp. 18–21, 71–91; McSeveney, *Politics of Depression*, pp. 3-31.

83. Richard Jensen, "Armies, Admen, and Crusaders: Types of Presidential Election Campaigns," *The History Teacher* 2 (Jan. 1969): 34.

84. Richard J. Jensen, *The Winning of the Midwest: Social and Political Conflict, 1888-1896* (Chicago, Ill.: University of Chicago Press, 1971), pp. 11-12.

85. Jensen, *Winning of the Midwest*, pp. 164-65.

86. John M. Taylor, *Garfield of Ohio: The Available Man* (New York: W.W. Norton, 1970), p. 200.

87. Jensen, *Winning of the Midwest*, pp. 13-14; Harry J. Sievers, *Benjamin Harrison*, vol. 2, *Hoosier Statesman: From the Civil War to the White House, 1865-1888* (New York: University Publishers, 1959), pp. 371, 423-25; Edmund B. Sullivan, *Hell-Bent for the White House* (Stamford, Conn.: Champion International Corp., 1988), pp. 80-83.

88. Jensen, *Winning of the Midwest*, pp. 165, 173; Jensen, "Armies, Admen, and Crusaders," p. 43; McGerr, *Decline of Popular Politics*, pp. 69-106.

89. Jensen, *Winning of the Midwest*, p. 174; McGerr, *Decline of Popular Politics*, p. 147.

90. Quoted in McGerr, *Decline of Popular Politics*, p. 151.

91. Fischer, *Tippecanoe and Trinkets Too*, p. 151.

92. See, e.g., John Hope Franklin, "Election of 1868," and William Gillette, "Election of 1872," in Schlesinger, *History of American Presidential Elections*, 2:1264-65, 1326.

93. Jensen, *Winning of the Midwest*, p. 274.

94. Jensen, *Winning of the Midwest*, pp. 288-89; McGerr, *Decline of Popular Politics*, pp. 140-41.

95. Benjamin Harrison to Whitelaw Reid, Oct. 9, 1888, in Sievers, *Benjamin Harrison*, 2:405-6.

96. Williams, "Politics of the Gilded Age," p. 116.

97. Jensen, *Winning of the Midwest*, p. 288.

98. Fischer and Sullivan, *American Political Ribbons and Ribbon Badges*, p. 264; Fischer, *Tippecanoe and Trinkets Too*, pp. 144-45; DeWitt, *Century of Campaign Buttons*, p. i; Sullivan, *American Political Badges and Medalets*, p. vii.

99. Melder, *Hail to the Candidate*, pp. 38-39; Edmund B. Sullivan, *Collecting Political Americana* (New York: Crown Publishers, Inc., 1980), pp. 32-36.

100. Fischer, *Tippecanoe and Trinkets Too*, pp. 155, 157.

101. McGerr, "Political Style and Women's Power," p. 869; McGerr, *Decline of Popular Politics*; Jensen, "Armies, Admen, and Crusaders," pp. 33-50; Jensen, *Winning of the Midwest*, p. 175.

102. Wiebe, *Self-Rule*, p. 71.

103. Henry F. Pringle, *Theodore Roosevelt: A Biography* (New York: Harcourt, Brace, and Company, 1931), pp. 4, 32, 490.

104. Lewis L. Gould, *The Modern American Presidency* (Lawrence, Kans.: University Press of Kansas, 2003), p. 33.

105. Pringle, *Theodore Roosevelt*, p. 137.

106. Kornbluh, *Why America Stopped Voting*, pp. 89-90, 97-98.

107. Kornbluh, *Why America Stopped Voting*, pp. 98-99; William E. Gienapp, "'Politics Seem to Enter Into Everything: Political Culture in the North, 1840-1860," in Stephen E. Maizlish and John G. Kushma, eds., *Essays on American Antebellum Politics, 1840-1860* (College Station, Tex.: Texas A&M University Press for the University of Texas at Arlington, 1982), pp. 20-21.

108. Walter LaFeber, "Election of 1900," in Schlesinger, *History of American Presidential Elections*, 3:1878; Kleppner, *Who Voted?*, p. 55.

109. Quoted in Kleppner, *Who Voted?*, p. 55.

110. Lionel E. Fredman, *The Australian Ballot: The Story of an American Reform* (East Lansing, Mich.: Michigan State University Press, 1968), pp. 83-84.

111. Kleppner, *Who Voted?*, pp. 60-61, 73.

112. J. Morgan Kousser, *The Shaping of Southern Politics: Suffrage Restriction and the Establishment of the One-Party South, 1880-1910* (New Haven, Conn.: Yale University Press, 1974). In 1896, there were 130,334 registered black voters in Louisiana; in 1904, there were 1,342.

113. McGerr, *Decline of Popular Politics*, pp. 152, 177.

114. Kornbluh, *Why America Stopped Voting*, pp. 111-15.

115. Dallek, *Hail to the Chief*, p. 4.

116. Francis Russell, *The Shadow of Blooming Grove: Warren G. Harding in His Times* (New York: McGraw-Hill, 1968), pp. 398-418; Samuel Hopkins Adams, *Incredible Era: The Life and Times of Warren Gamaliel Harding* (Boston: Houghton Mifflin, 1939), pp. 170-78; Donald R. McCoy, "Election of 1920," in Schlesinger, *History of American Presidential Elections*, 3:2370-85.

117. McGerr, *Decline of Popular Politics*, p. 166.

118. John Gunther, *Taken at the Flood: The Story of Albert D. Lasker* (New York: Harper, 1960), p. 112; McGerr, *Decline of Popular Politics*, p. 170.

119. Edward W. Chester, *Radio, Television, and American Politics* (New York: Sheed and Ward, 1969), pp. 3, 9, 16; Jamieson, *Packaging the Presidency*, p. 25.

120. Jamieson, *Packaging the Presidency*, p. 24; Chester, *Radio, Television, and American Politics*, pp. 9-23. Radio also tended to shorten both speeches and sentences, ending the day of the great nineteenth-century orator.

121. William E. Leuchtenburg, *Franklin D. Roosevelt and the New Deal* (New York: Harper and Row, 1963), p. 331.

122. Jensen, *Grassroots Politics*, p. 12.

123. Campbell, Converse, Miller, and Stokes, *American Voter*, pp. 153-67; Kleppner, *Who Voted?*, pp. 84-89.

124. Fischer, *Tippecanoe and Trinkets Too*, p. 244.

125. Freedom Forum Media Studies Center, *The Homestretch: New Politics. New Media. New Voters?* (New York: Columbia University Press, 1992), p. 55.

126. Charles A. H. Thomson, *Television and Presidential Politics: The Experience in 1952 and the Problems Ahead* (Washington, DC: The Brookings Institution, 1956), pp. 4–5; Gilbert Vivian Seldes, *The Great Audience* (New York: Viking Press, 1950), p. 207. Later, the delegates quietly returned and put on their badges again.

127. Larry J. Sabato, *The Rise of Political Consultants: New Ways of Winning Elections* (New York: Basic Books, 1981), p. 112.

128. Thomson, *Television and Presidential Politics*, pp. 1–2.

129. Patterson, *Vanishing Voter*, p. 16.

130. Patterson, *Vanishing Voter*, p. 16.

131. G. Cotler, "That Plague of Spots on Madison Avenue," *Reporter* (Nov. 1942): 7-8.

132. Edwin Diamond and Stephen Bates, *The Spot: The Rise of Political Advertising on Television* (Cambridge, Mass.: MIT Press, 1984), pp. ix, 57; Robert Spero, *The Duping of the American Voter: Dishonesty & Deception in Presidential Television Advertising* (New York: Lippincott & Crowell, 1980), p. 37.

133. Jamieson, *Packaging the Presidency*, p. 85.

134. Jamieson, *Packaging the Presidency*, pp. 44, 97. Media consultants for both parties soon learned their lesson, solving the pre-emption problem in 1956 by using a five-minute "spot"; the networks simply shortened their programs so that the political "spots" did not cut directly into the program.

135. Sabato, *Rise of Political Consultants*, p. 114; Stephen Salmore and Barbara G. Salmore, *Candidates, Parties, and Campaigns: Electoral Politics in America* (Washington, D.C.: Congressional Quarterly Inc., 1985), p. 42. In constant dollars, Eisenhower in 1952 actually spent amounts on television comparable to candidates in the 1980s and 1990s: L. Patrick Devlin, "Political Commercials in American Presidential Elections," in Lynda Lee Kaid and Christina Holz-Bacha, eds., *Political Advertising in Western Democracies: Parties and Candidates on Television* (Thousand Oaks, Calif.: Sage Publications, 1995), pp. 189-90.

136. Jamieson, *Packaging the Presidency*, pp. 20, 95.

137. Sabato, *Rise of Political Consultants*, p. 124.

138. Sabato, *Rise of Political Consultants*, pp. 69-70.

139. Chester, *Radio, Television, and American Politics*, pp. 119-20; Theodore H. White, *The Making of the President, 1960* (New York: Athaneum Press, 1961), pp. 279-95.

140. Patterson, *Vanishing Voter*, p. 15. Even though the country had 100 million fewer people in 1960 than in 2000, more viewers tuned in to the Kennedy-Nixon debates than watched the Bush-Gore debates.

141. Stephen Ansolabehere and Shanto Iyengar, *Going Negative: How Attack Ads Shrink and Polarize the Electorate* (New York: The Free Press, 1995), pp. 1-2; Patterson, *Vanishing Voter*, p. 48.

142. Jamieson, *Dirty Politics*, pp. 22-23.

143. Theodore H. White, *America in Search of Itself: The Making of the President, 1956-1980* (New York: Harper & Row, 1982), p. 165.

144. Sabato, *Rise of Political Consultants*, p. 117; DiClerico, *Political Parties, Campaigns, and Elections*, p. 93; Joanne Morreale, *Presidential Campaign Film*, p. 1.

145. E. D. Dover, *Presidential Elections in the Television Age, 1960–1992* (Westport, Conn.: Praeger, 1994), pp. 6-20; Marion R. Just, Ann N. Krigler, Dean E. Alger, Timothy E. Cook, Montague Kern, and Darrell West, "Discourse and Decision," in DiClerico, *Political Parties, Campaigns, and Elections*, p. 186.

146. S. Robert Lichter and Richard E. Noyes, "There They Go Again: Media Coverage of Campaign '96," in DiClerico, *Political Parties, Campaigns, and Elections*, pp. 96-97.

147. Patterson, *Vanishing Voter*, p. 68.

148. Dover, *Presidential Elections in the Television Age*, p. 17.

149. Kevin Phillips, *The Emerging Republican Majority* (New Rochelle, N.Y.: Arlington House, 1969); Dover, *Presidential Elections in the Television Age*, p. 35.

150. Thomas, *Pursuit of the White House*, p. 163; Theodore H. White, *The Making of the President, 1972* (New York: Athaneum Publishers, 1973), pp. 342-43.

151. Fischer, *Tippecanoe and Trinkets Too*, pp. 235, 274-78. Ironically, another reason that campaign buttons almost disappeared was the popularity of polyester double-knit fabrics for clothing, which were easily damaged by the pins on the back of the buttons. As a result, some campaigns began to issue disposable lapel stickers, including one in 1968 that said, "If I Had a Button, It Would Say Humphrey-Muskie."

152. Lewis L. Gould, *Grand Old Party: A History of the Republicans* (New York: Random House, 2003), pp. 401–02, 411.

153. William E. Pemberton, *Exit with Honor: The Life and Presidency of Ronald Reagan* (Armonk, N.Y.: M.E. Sharpe, 1997), p. 69.

154. Dover, *Presidential Elections in the Television Age*, p. 24.

155. Gould, *Grand Old Party*, pp. 438-39.

156. Gould, *Grand Old Party*, p. 470.

157. Marion R. Just, Ann N. Krigler, Dean E. Alger, Timothy E. Cook, Montague Kern, and Darrell West, "Discourse and Decision," in DiClerico, *Political Parties, Campaigns, and Elections*, p. 184.

158. Morris P. Fiorina, "The Causes and Consequences of Divided Government: Lessons of 1992-1994," in DiClerico, *Political Parties, Campaigns, and Elections*, p. 286.

159. U.S. Census Bureau, *Statistical Abstract of the United States: 2002* (Washington, D.C.: G.P.O., 2002), p. 254; Committee for the Study of the American Electorate, *Battleground State Mobilization Efforts Propel Voter Turnout Slightly Upward in Historic but Disturbing Election*, http://www.gspm.org/csae/cgans6.htm, pp. 1-5.

160. Patterson, *Vanishing Voter*, pp. 3-4; U.S. Census Bureau, *Statistical Abstract of the United States: 2002*, p. 254.

161. Patterson, *Vanishing Voter*, p. 13. In the 2002 congressional elections, 74.7 million people, or 39 percent of eligible voters, went to the polls: *Statistics of the Congressional Election of November 5, 2002, Showing the Vote Cast for Each Nominee for United States Senator, Representative, and Delegate to the One Hundred Eighth Congress...* (Washington, D.C., 2003), http://clerk.house.gov, pp. 51-53; http://www.washingtonpost.com/wp-srv/politics/daily/graphics/voterturnout_110802.html, "Voter Turnout."

162. Haynes Johnson, *The Best of Times: America in the Clinton Years* (New York: Harcourt, 2001), p. 521.

163. Steven J. Rosenstone and John Mark Hansen, *Mobilization, Participation, and Democracy in America* (New York: MacMillan Publishing Co., 1993), pp. 2, 211-12, 229-30. While barely fifty percent of Americans vote in presidential elections, between eighty and ninety percent of the electorates vote in Austria, Belgium, Germany, and Portugal, seventy to eighty percent in Ireland, France, the United Kingdom, and Japan. In some of these countries, of course, people are required by law to vote.

164. Ladd, "Participation in American Elections," in Rogers, *Voting and the Spirit of American Democracy*, pp. 115-16; Pomper and Lederman, *Elections in America*, p. 35.

165. Keyssar, *Right to Vote*, pp. 314-16; Patterson, *Vanishing Voter*, p. 8.

166. U.S. Department of Commerce, Economics and Statistics Administration, U.S. Census Bureau, "Voting and Registration in the Election of November 2000" (Washington, D.C.: G.P.O., 2002), pp. 9-10; Patterson, *Vanishing Voter*, p. 133. The states with same-day registration are Idaho, Maine, Minnesota, New Hampshire, Wisconsin, and Wyoming.

167. Frank J. Sorauf, *Party Politics in America* (Boston: Little, Brown, 1968), pp. 174-97; Frances Fox Piven and Richard A. Cloward, *Why Americans Don't Vote* (New York: Pantheon Books, 1988); Ladd, "Participation in American Elections," in Rogers, *Voting and the Spirit of American Democracy*, p. 117.

168. U.S. Department of Commerce, "Voting and Registration in the Election of November 2000," pp. 11-14; *Presidential Elections Since 1789*, pp. 87-88.

169. *Presidential Elections Since 1789*, p. 88; Warren E. Miller and J. Merrill Shanks, *The New American Voter* (Cambridge, Mass.: Harvard University Press, 1996), pp. 90-94; Ruy T. Tiexiera, "Just How Much Difference Does Turnout Really Make?" in DiClerico, *Poitical Parties, Campaigns, and Elections*, p. 143; Doppelt and Shearer, *Nonvoters*, p. 17. In the last half-century, social status and education have become the most effective predictors of political involvement: Kornbluh, *Why America Stopped Voting*, p. 108.

170. U.S. Department of Commerce, "Voting and Registration in the Election of November 2000," p. 5.

171. Patterson, *Vanishing Voter*, p. 11.

172. Freedom Forum Media Studies Center, *Homestretch*, p. 3; Kleppner, *Who Voted?*, pp. 131-33.

173. Doppelt and Shearer, *Nonvoters*, p. 2; Freedom Forum Media Studies Center, *Homestretch*, pp. 22, 26.

174. Sara Hunter Graham, *Woman Suffrage and the New Democracy* (New Haven, Conn.: Yale University Press, 1996), p. 160; Patterson, *Vanishing Voter*, p. 36.

175. Patterson, *Vanishing Voter*, p. 36.

176. Thomas E. Patterson, *The Mass Media Election: How Americans Choose Their President* (New York: Praeger, 1980), p. 4; Darrell M. West, *Air Wars: Television Advertising in Election Campaigns, 1952-1992* (Washington, D.C.: Congressional Quarterly, Inc., 1993), p. 6; *Presidential Elections Since 1789*, p. 5; Patterson, *Vanishing Voter*, p. 139.

177. Sabato, *Rise of Political Consultants*, pp. 221-22; Jensen, *Grassroots Politics*, pp. 22-23.

178. Sullivan, *Hell-Bent for the Whitehouse*, p. 4.

ITEM 15
William McKinley celluloid medallion mounted on ribbons, 1896 election.

Electing and Collecting

The Hervey A. Priddy Collection of
American Presidential & Political Memorabilia at Bridwell Library

★

HERVEY A. PRIDDY

Buttons, stickers, and songs...are the sparkle and glitter
of which campaigns are made. ED KOCH, 1977

I PROBABLY HAVE A TOUCH OF THE COLLECTOR in my genes, for my family, especially my father, passed on to me a fascination with historical things. But it takes more than an inborn predilection to become an avid collector. Someone or something must provide the necessary nudge, the spark, to inspire an individual to put together a specialized collection. For me, the nudge came in the wake of a career change. In the 1980s, I left the business world and decided to enter academia. During the first stage of my journey, I audited a course at SMU on twentieth-century United States presidential politics, which was so fascinating that it unlocked a latent love of history, particularly American political history. While taking the course, I happened to travel to New Orleans, where I ventured into a small shop that specialized in nineteenth- and twentieth-century political Americana. The buttons, ribbons, and pins I saw there brought to life the candidates, issues, and elections I had been studying. Several hours later, I walked out of the shop with a sack full of buttons and a brand new passion, collecting presidential campaign memorabilia.

Since that day my collection has grown steadily and now includes nineteenth- and twentieth-century posters, tokens, leaflets, banners, textiles, toys, ceramics, lapel devices, and commemoratives.

Like most collectors, I find certain items in the collection especially compelling. One is a group of nineteenth-century campaign lapel devices called ferrotypes. Usually about one inch in diameter, punched with a hole so they could be suspended from the lapel, ferrotypes feature the presidential nominee's image on one side and the vice presidential nominee's on the other, encased in brass. They first appeared in the late 1850s, soon after the tintype process of photography was invented. The advantage of photographic likenesses was not lost on candidates—it familiarized distant voters with their names and faces—and over the next two decades campaigners produced a wide variety of ferrotypes.

I am fortunate that I was able to collect ferrotypes of all the 1860 nominees: Stephen A. Douglas and Herschell Johnson (Democratic, Northern); John Breckinridge and Joseph Lane (Democratic, Southern); John Bell and Edward Everett (Constitutional Union); and Abraham Lincoln and Hannibal Hamlin (Republican). Also included in the collection is an 1864 Lincoln and Andrew Johnson ferrotype. The two different images of Lincoln are telling. In the 1860 ferrotype he is almost a stranger to modern eyes, plain, clean-shaven, and youthful, but in the 1864 button, he is much more the familiar bearded giant, sadly aged by the Civil War.

ITEM 16
Grover Cleveland
medalet, 1885
inauguration.

Although their popularity would wane after the introduction of ferrotypes, political medallic pieces or medalets were widely circulated in the nineteenth century. Either worn on the lapel (these have a hole for a ribbon) or carried as pocket pieces, medalets vary in size from three-fourths to one and one-half inches and exist in several materials. Among the more entertaining is an 1885 post-election white metal piece that pokes fun at the winner, Democrat Grover Cleveland, and his principal opponent, Republican James G. Blaine. Similar in shape, size, and color to the modern day quarter, the piece features the image of a bull on one side, under which is written "Beef Takes The Presidential Chair March 4, 1885" and below, in smaller letters, "R.R.R. Did It." The image of the bull and "Beef" alludes to the Republicans' slogan "We Go for Brains, not Beef" (Cleveland was portly). The "R.R.R. Did It" recalls the infamous slur against Democrats, the party of "rum, Romanism, and rebellion," made by a Protestant clergyman, Reverend Samuel Burchard, which cost Blaine dearly.

A group of campaign materials that I take great pride in was produced for the 1896 election. This exciting campaign, one of the most important in our history, pitted Republican William McKinley against Democrat William Jennings Bryan. Remembered as the "battle of the standards," the campaign centered on the "money issue," or gold versus silver. Bryan and his supporters wanted the gold standard replaced with the unlimited coinage of silver at a ratio of sixteen ounces of silver to one ounce of gold. McKinley, on the other hand, sought to uphold the gold standard. In my view, the political memorabilia produced on behalf of the candidates and the currency issue cover the widest range of creativity for any American presidential campaign.

ITEM 17
Mechanical
flag waver,
1896 election.

An interesting item is a Republican two-piece mechanical "broken dollar" lapel device, which contrasts sound money with free silver. When the hanger is rotated the message changes from "Free Silver Means A Dollar Worth 50 Cents" (anti-Bryan) to "Sound Money Means A Dollar Worth 100 Cents" (pro-McKinley). Other interesting lapel devices include several ingenious mechanical shell badges. In one, a red, white, and blue enameled flag snaps open to reveal pictures of McKinley and his running mate, Garret Hobart. In another, lifting a brass blanket on a GOP elephant shows an image of McKinley. The most popular 1896 mechanical badges were, by far, brass "gold bugs" and silvered brass "silver bugs" shaped like beetles. When the catch on the Republican gold bug is touched the wings spring open to display images of McKinley and Hobart, and when the silver bug is opened a picture of Bryan appears on one wing and the Democratic slogan "16 to 1" on the other.

The "16 to 1" slogan also appeared in 1896 on another new campaign lapel device, the celluloid pin-back button. Patented in the mid-1890s, the buttons were produced by covering a lightweight metal disk—usually about one inch in diameter—with a paper image. A thin clear piece of celluloid was spread over the paper and both the paper and celluloid were then curled around the back of the disk, and held by a metal ring. A spring-wire pin for pinning the button to the lapel was attached to the metal ring. Inexpensive, imaginative, and easily distributed, pin-back buttons quickly became the most widely used campaign gadget. Although celluloid buttons were replaced by lithographed buttons in the 1920s, the basic design of the campaign pin-back button has changed little over the last century.

ITEM 18
"16 to 1" celluloid pin-back button, 1896 election.

In 1896 gold-and-silver issue celluloid buttons were the most popular campaign items, but a number of colorful jugate buttons (buttons with images of two candidates side by side) were also produced, including one of the most unusual I have run across. Measuring four and one-half by six and one-half inches, it is one of the largest celluloid buttons ever produced. William McKinley and the man who oversaw his campaign, Mark Hanna, are pictured on the button, but what is interesting here is that Hanna, the campaign manager, actually appears in front of the candidate, McKinley.

It has not been unusual, however, for non-presidential candidates to appear with presidents on campaign materials. Office seekers have been attempting to ride the coattails of revered presidents for more than a century. No one did it better than our own state's Lyndon B. Johnson, who raised the practice to an art form. Several items in my collection exemplify his mastery. One is a two and one-half inch lithographed button from Johnson's first United States Senate campaign in 1941. On a white background, red, white, and blue letters spell out "Me and Roosevelt for Johnson," above large images of President Franklin D. Roosevelt and Johnson. The second item is also from the 1941 race. Dropped from an airplane at a Johnson rally in Texas, the 6 x 9 inch leaflet says, "This is not a bomb, but it could happen here. Vote for Lyndon B. Johnson and help Franklin D. Roosevelt defend America from Enemy Bombs." The message was clear—a vote for Johnson was a vote for Roosevelt's programs and protection from the dangers looming in Europe and the Pacific.

ITEM 19
Franklin D. Roosevelt *&* Lyndon B. Johnson button, 1941 U.S. Senate election.

I take special pride in the large number of inaugural medals in the collection, for they are among the most difficult (and, I must say, expensive) items to collect. Individuals and the United States Mint issued many "unofficial" inaugural medals until 1896, when an inaugural committee for the first time sanctioned the design, production, and distribution of an "official" inaugural medal. I have been fortunate enough to acquire the Official Inaugural Medals for every president from 1897 to 2001, including those who assumed office upon the death or resignation of the sitting president. Several of these acquisitions presented great challenges since the number of medals minted was quite small. The rarest pieces are those issued for Presidents Woodrow Wilson (second term), Warren Harding, Calvin Coolidge, and Herbert Hoover.

With fewer than seventy struck, the 1921 Harding medal is the scarcest of all the presidential inaugural medals. This had not been the Republicans' original plan. Soon after

ITEM 20
Warren G. Harding
official silver medal,
1921 inauguration.

ITEM 21
Theodore Roosevelt
Saint-Gaudens/Weinman
bronze medal,
1905 inauguration.

Harding triumphed over Democrat James S. Cox in the 1920 presidential election, he set the Inauguration Committee to work planning a grand celebration that would help put Americans back on the road to what he called "normalcy." The celebration would include a parade, a lavish ball, a concert, and spectacular fireworks, the likes of which had not been seen in Washington for a generation. To reward those who would help with the celebration, the committee directed that the tradition of giving replicas in bronze of the President's inaugural medal be restored. But before the plans could be carried out, the American economy soured and millions of workers were thrown out of work. Under intense pressure, Harding cancelled the parade and the fireworks display. The Inauguration Committee also lowered its sights, and only two or three gold medals were struck, around four in silver, and fewer than sixty in bronze. Included in my collection is one of the four silver Harding medals known to exist.

Theodore Roosevelt aided collectors, however, by issuing two inaugural medals in 1905. The first was very similar to the 1901 Roosevelt medal struck by the United States Mint. Unhappy with the design, Roosevelt asked the renowned American sculptor Augustus Saint-Gaudens to design a more artistic medal. Saint-Gaudens accepted the challenge and with the assistance of another sculptor, Adolph Weinman, who executed Saint-Gaudens' design, and Louis Comfort Tiffany, whose firm Tiffany & Company cast the medals, produced a Renaissance-style medal. On the side of the three-inch medal that bears the likeness of Roosevelt are the Latin words "Aequum Cuique," meaning "To Each What Is Equal" or, with a little imagination, "Square Deal," Roosevelt's name for his domestic initiatives. On the reverse is an eagle, which would appear again in 1907 on the $10 gold piece Saint-Gaudens designed for the United States Mint. The Saint-Gaudens/Weinman medals are, as the 1905 Inaugural Committee's final report states, "superb works of art."

Building this collection has been, and continues to be, great fun. It is a privilege to have the collection housed at the extraordinary Bridwell Library, but librarians beware, I am not yet finished collecting. I am grateful to Valerie Hotchkiss, the Director of the Library, and James McMillin, the Associate Director, for their interest in the collection and for their eagerness to see its continued growth, and to Hermann Michaeli for his work organizing the items. I have the best of all possible worlds for a collector: I can continue to build the collection, while the items are well cared for, accessible to scholars, and, best of all, out of my wife's way at home! It has also been fun to work with my esteemed mentor R. Hal Williams of the SMU Department of History in curating this exhibit.

As a collector, I often try to place myself in the position of the person who once wore a campaign item in support of his political party and candidate. Past issues were just as complex as the ones we face today. In designing their campaign pieces, however, the political parties and candidates forced themselves to boil down the issues to a few important words or phrases, which could be displayed on a vest, attached to a pole, or shown on a street corner. For better or worse, those campaign slogans have driven American presidential campaigns for over two centuries. I like to believe that it is the dedication, interest, and concerns of the voters that are the most compelling forces behind the campaign materials that you see in this exhibition. Every vote still counts, and it is with that thought in mind, so vital to both the past and the future of the American republic, that I dedicate the exhibition, and my collection, to the American voter.

ITEM 22
Blanche Merrill, *We Take Our Hats Off To You—Mr. Wilson*, 1914.

Checklist of Items

1789 INAUGURATION
George Washington.
Commemorative brass clothing buttons.
Bridwell Library Special Collections and loan from
the Museum of American Political Life, University
of Hartford.

1792
Second Congress of the United States.
*An Act Relative to the Election of a President
and Vice-President of the United States.*
Philadelphia: 24 October 1791, approved
1 March 1792.
Signed in ink by Thomas Jefferson, U.S. Secretary
of State.
Loan from Joe Rubinfine, West Palm Beach, Florida.

1795
George Washington.
Autograph letter signed to Timothy Pickering,
U.S. Secretary of War.
Mount Vernon, Virginia, 27 July 1795.
Loan from the Harlan Crow Library, Dallas, Texas.

1798
Gilbert Stuart, *George Washington*, 1798.
Oil on canvas.
Loan from the Harlan Crow Library, Dallas, Texas.

1800 ELECTION
William Linn, *Serious Considerations on the
Election of a President: Addressed to the Citizens
of the United States* (New York: L. Furman, 1800).
Bridwell Library Special Collections.

1809 INAUGURATION
James Madison (Democratic-Republican).
Presidential inaugural address.
Reprinted in *The Philadelphia Aurora*,
7 March 1809.
Bridwell Library Special Collections.

1828 ELECTION
Andrew Jackson (Democratic).
Autograph letter signed to Reverend Finis Ewing.
Hermitage, Tennessee, 17 November 1828.
Loan from the Harlan Crow Library, Dallas, Texas.

1828 ELECTION
Andrew Jackson (Democratic).
"Andrew Jackson/The Hero of New Orleans"
glazed ceramic pitcher.
Loan from the Smithsonian Institution,
National Museum of American History, Behring
Center.

1828 ELECTION
Andrew Jackson (Democratic).
"Glorious Victory" handbill.
Bridwell Library Special Collections.

1829 INAUGURATION
Andrew Jackson (Democratic).
"Andrew Jackson/Magnanimous in Peace/
Victorious in War" cotton chintz textile.
Bridwell Library Special Collections.

1832 ELECTION
Andrew Jackson (Democratic).
"King Andrew the First" lithograph broadside.
Loan from the Museum of American Political Life,
University of Hartford.

1833 INAUGURATION
Andrew Jackson (Democratic).
Silver inaugural medalet.
Bridwell Library, The Hervey A. Priddy Collection.

1840 ELECTION
William Henry Harrison (Whig).
Log Cabin ceramic tea set.
Loan from the Smithsonian Institution, National
Museum of American History, Behring Center.

1840 ELECTION
William Henry Harrison (Whig).
Log Cabin cotton chintz textile.
Bridwell Library Special Collections.

1844 ELECTION
James K. Polk and George M. Dallas (Democratic).
White metal holed medalet.
Bridwell Library, The Hervey A. Priddy Collection.

1844 ELECTION
James K. Polk and George M. Dallas (Democratic).
Cotton flag banner.
Loan from the Smithsonian Institution, National
Museum of American History, Behring Center.

1844 ELECTION
Henry Clay (Whig).
"Young Men's National Whig Convention" silk
ribbon badge.
Loan from the Museum of American Political Life,
University of Hartford.

1844 ELECTION
Henry Clay and Theodore Frelinghuysen (Whig).
"Same Old Coon" cotton flag banner.
Loan from the Museum of American Political Life,
University of Hartford.

1844 ELECTION
James K. Polk (Democratic).
"Young Hickory of Tennessee" silk ribbon.
Bridwell Library, The Hervey A. Priddy Collection.

1845 INAUGURATION
James K. Polk (Democratic).
Copper inaugural medal.
Bridwell Library, The Hervey A. Priddy Collection.

1848 ELECTION
General Lewis Cass (Democratic).
"United We Stand" brass holed medalet.
Bridwell Library, The Hervey A. Priddy Collection.

c. 1852
James B. Walker and Donald Kirkpatrick
(American/Know-Nothing).
"Know-Nothing" campaign ticket.
Bridwell Library Special Collections.

c. 1850s
George Caleb Bingham, *County Election*, c. 1850s.
Lithograph (after the oil painting of 1852).
Loan from the Amon Carter Museum, Fort Worth.

c. 1850s
George Caleb Bingham, *Stump Speaking*, c. 1850s.
Lithograph (after the oil painting of 1854).
Loan from the Amon Carter Museum, Fort Worth.

c.1850s
George Caleb Bingham, *Verdict of the People*,
c. 1850s.
Lithograph (after the oil painting of 1854).
Loan from the Amon Carter Museum, Fort Worth.

c. 1850s
George Caleb Bingham, *Canvassing for a Vote*,
c. 1850s.
Lithograph (after the oil painting of 1855).
Loan from the Amon Carter Museum, Fort Worth.

1856 ELECTION
Millard Fillmore (American/Know-Nothing).
K N Quick Step.
New York: Winner & Shuster, 1854.
Loan from the Smithsonian Institution, National
Museum of American History, Behring Center.

1856 ELECTION
John Frémont (Republican).
"Free Soil & Free Speech" bronze medalet.
Bridwell Library, The Hervey A. Priddy Collection.

1856 ELECTION
Jessie Benton Frémont and John C. Frémont
(Republican).
"Frémont and Jessie" hand-made of linen and
paper poster.
Loan from the Museum of American Political Life,
University of Hartford.

1857 INAUGURATION
James Buchanan (Democratic).
White metal inaugural medal.
Bridwell Library, The Hervey A. Priddy Collection.

1860 ELECTION
Abraham Lincoln (Republican).
"Rail Splitter From The West" brass holed medalet.
Bridwell Library, The Hervey A. Priddy Collection.

1860 ELECTION
Abraham Lincoln (Republican).
"Free Homes for Free Men" brass medalet.
Bridwell Library, The Hervey A. Priddy Collection.

1860 ELECTION
Abraham Lincoln (Republican).
Wide-Awake Parade wood engraving.
Harper's Weekly, 16 October 1860.
Loan from the Fondren Library, Southern Methodist
University.

1860 ELECTION
Abraham Lincoln (Republican).
Wide-Awake parade cape.
Loan from the Smithsonian Institution, National
Museum of American History, Behring Center.

1860 ELECTION
Abraham Lincoln (Republican).
Max Mayo, *The Wide-Awake Quick Step.*
Albany: A. & D. R. Andrews, 1860.
Loan from the Museum of American Political Life,
University of Hartford.

1860 ELECTION
Abraham Lincoln (Republican).
Wide-Awake parade torchlight.
Loan from the Museum of American Political Life,
University of Hartford.

1860 ELECTION
Stephen Douglas and Herschel V. Johnson
(Democratic).
Brass encased ferrotype.
Bridwell Library, The Hervey A. Priddy Collection.

1860 ELECTION
Abraham Lincoln and Hannibal Hamlin
(Republican).
Brass encased ferrotype.
Bridwell Library, The Hervey A. Priddy Collection.

1860 ELECTION
John Bell & Edward Everett (Constitutional Union).
Brass encased ferrotype.
Bridwell Library, The Hervey A. Priddy Collection.

1860 ELECTION
John C. Breckinridge and Joseph Lane
(Southern Democratic).

Brass encased ferrotype.
Bridwell Library, The Hervey A. Priddy Collection.

1860 ELECTION
Abraham Lincoln (Republican).
Primitive hand-made of leather ribbon.
Loan from the Smithsonian Institution, National
Museum of American History, Behring Center.

1864 ELECTION
John C. Frémont and John Cochrane (Republican).
Brass encased ferrotype.
Bridwell Library, The Hervey A. Priddy Collection.

1864 ELECTION
Abraham Lincoln and Andrew Johnson (National
Union/Republican).
Brass encased ferrotype.
Bridwell Library, The Hervey A. Priddy Collection.

1864 ELECTION
Abraham Lincoln and Andrew Johnson
(National Union/Republican).
Electoral ticket.
Loan from the Museum of American Political Life,
University of Hartford.

1864 ELECTION
Abraham Lincoln and Andrew Johnson
(National Union/Republican).
"Union candidates" white metal medalet.
Bridwell Library, The Hervey A. Priddy Collection.

1865 INAUGURATION
Abraham Lincoln and Andrew Johnson
(National Union/Republican).
Inaugural ball invitation.
Bridwell Library, The Hervey A. Priddy Collection.

1865
Salmon P. Chase, Chief Justice of the U.S. Supreme
Court.
Autograph manuscript signed.
Washington D.C., 15 April 1865.
Loan from the Harlan Crow Library, Dallas, Texas.

1868 ELECTION
Ulysses S. Grant (Republican).
Portrait shell badge.
Bridwell Library, The Hervey A. Priddy Collection.

1896 ELECTION
William McKinley and Garret A. Hobart
(Republican).
"GOP" elephant-shaped jugate mechanical shell
badge.
Bridwell Library, The Hervey A. Priddy Collection.

1896 ELECTION
William McKinley and Garret A. Hobart
(Republican).
"Republican County Election" jugate celluloid
medallion with ribbon and hanger.
Bridwell Library, The Hervey A. Priddy Collection.

1896 ELECTION
William McKinley and Garret A. Hobart
(Republican).
"Gold Standard/Protection" jugate celluloid
pin-back button.
Bridwell Library, The Hervey A. Priddy Collection.

1896 ELECTION
William McKinley and Garret A. Hobart
(Republican).
"We Want the Money" celluloid pin-back button.
Bridwell Library, The Hervey A. Priddy Collection.

1896 ELECTION
William McKinley and Garret A. Hobart
(Republican).
"Sound Money" brass shell badge.
Bridwell Library, The Hervey A. Priddy Collection.

1896 ELECTION
William McKinley and Garret A. Hobart
(Republican).
"96/Sound Money/Protection" lapel stud.
Bridwell Library, The Hervey A. Priddy Collection.

1896 ELECTION
William Jennings Bryan and Arthur Sewall
(Democratic).
"16 to 1" jugate celluloid pin-back button.
Bridwell Library, The Hervey A. Priddy Collection.

1896 ELECTION
William Jennings Bryan and Arthur Sewall
(Democratic).
"16 to 1" jugate celluloid pin-back button.
Bridwell Library, The Hervey A. Priddy Collection.

1896 ELECTION
William Jennings Bryan and Arthur Sewall
(Democratic).
"Our Candidates" celluloid pin-back button.
Bridwell Library, The Hervey A. Priddy Collection.

1896 ELECTION
William Jennings Bryan and Arthur Sewall
(Democratic).
"16 to 1" celluloid pin-back button.
Bridwell Library, The Hervey A. Priddy Collection.

1896 ELECTION
William Jennings Bryan (Democratic).
"Government Dollar" money piece.
Bridwell Library Special Collections.

1896 ELECTION
William Jennings Bryan (Democratic).
Silver bug-shaped mechanical shell badge.
Bridwell Library, The Hervey A. Priddy Collection.

1896 ELECTION
William McKinley and Mark Hanna (Republican).
Jugate celluloid pin-back button.
Bridwell Library, The Hervey A. Priddy Collection.

1896 ELECTION
New York state presidential ballot.
Bridwell Library Special Collections.

1897 INAUGURATION
William McKinley (Republican).
Inaugural ball invitation.
Bridwell Library, The Hervey A. Priddy Collection.

1897 INAUGURATION
William McKinley (Republican).
Inaugural ball program.
Bridwell Library, The Hervey A. Priddy Collection.

1900 ELECTION
William McKinley and Theodore Roosevelt
(Republican).
"Full Dinner Bucket" celluloid pin-back button.
Bridwell Library, The Hervey A. Priddy Collection.

1900 ELECTION
William J. Bryan & Adlai E. Stevenson (Democratic).
Jugate celluloid pin-back button.
Bridwell Library, The Hervey A. Priddy Collection.

1900 ELECTION
William McKinley and Theodore Roosevelt
(Republican).
"Hamilton County Republican Candidates" poster.
Bridwell Library Special Collections.

1900 ELECTION
William McKinley and Theodore Roosevelt
(Republican).
Fred Spencer, *McKinley and Roosevelt March.*
Howley, Haviland, & Co., 1900.
Bridwell Library, The Decherd Turner Collection.

1901 INAUGURATION
William McKinley (Republican).
Official silver inaugural medal.
Bridwell Library, The Hervey A. Priddy Collection.

1901 INAUGURATION
Theodore Roosevelt (Republican).
Official bronze inaugural medal.
Bridwell Library, The Hervey A. Priddy Collection.

1904 ELECTION
Theodore Roosevelt (Republican).
Byron Andrews, *Facts about the Candidate.*
Chicago: Sam Stone, 1904.
Bridwell Library Special Collections.

1904 ELECTION
Alton B. Parker (Democratic).
Portrait celluloid pin-back button.
Bridwell Library, The Hervey A. Priddy Collection.

1904 ELECTION
Alton B. Parker and Henry G. Davis (Democratic).
Jugate celluloid pin-back button.
Bridwell Library, The Hervey A. Priddy Collection.

1905 INAUGURATION
Theodore Roosevelt (Republican).
Official bronze inaugural medal.
Bridwell Library, The Hervey A. Priddy Collection.

1905 INAUGURATION
Theodore Roosevelt (Republican).
Official Saint-Gaudens/Wernman bronze inaugural
medal.
Bridwell Library, The Hervey A. Priddy Collection.

1905 INAUGURATION
Theodore Roosevelt and Charles W. Fairbanks
(Republican).
Inaugural program.
Bridwell Library, The Hervey A. Priddy Collection.

1905
Benjamin W. Clinedinst, photograph of Theodore
Roosevelt, 1905.
Inscribed to Vice President Charles W. Fairbanks
and signed by Roosevelt, 3 March 1909.
Loan from the Harlan Crow Library, Dallas, Texas.

1908 ELECTION
William H. Taft (Republican).
"Our Next President" postcard.
Bridwell Library Special Collections.

1908 ELECTION
William H. Taft (Republican).
Portrait celluloid stickpin.
Bridwell Library, The Hervey A. Priddy Collection.

1908 ELECTION
Eugene V. Debs and Benjamin Hanford (Socialist).
Jugate celluloid pin-back button.
Bridwell Library, The Hervey A. Priddy Collection.

1908 ELECTION
William Jennings Bryan (Democratic).
Paper card novelty.
Loan from the Smithsonian Institution, National
Museum of American History, Behring Center.

1908 ELECTION
William Jennings Bryan (Democratic).
"Bottom Is Out of the Dinner Pail" postcard.
Bridwell Library, The Hervey A. Priddy Collection.

1909 INAUGURATION
William H. Taft & John S. Sherman (Republican).
Official bronze inaugural medal.
Bridwell Library, The Hervey A. Priddy Collection.

1912 ELECTION
Theodore Roosevelt (Progressive).
We Want Teddy cotton bandanna.
Loan from the Museum of American Political Life,
University of Hartford.

1913 INAUGURATION
Woodrow Wilson (Democratic).
Official bronze inaugural medal.
Bridwell Library, The Hervey A. Priddy Collection.

1916
Theodore Roosevelt.
Autographed signed letter to Henry A. Wise Wood.
Long Island, New York, 27 May 1916.
Loan from the Harlan Crow Library, Dallas, Texas.

1916 ELECTION
Woodrow Wilson (Democrat).
Blanche Merrill, *We Take Our Hats Off To You—Mr. Wilson.*
New York: Leo Feist, 1914.
Loan from Thomas J. Knock.

1916 ELECTION
Woodrow Wilson (Democratic).
"VI Invitiamo A Votare Per IL Presidente Wilson" foreign language poster (Italian).
Loan from the Museum of American Political Life, University of Hartford.

1917 INAUGURATION
Woodrow Wilson (Democratic).
Official bronze inaugural medal.
Bridwell Library, The Hervey A. Priddy Collection.

1920 ELECTION
Warren G. Harding and Calvin Coolidge (Republican).
"Our Choice" window decal.
Loan from the Museum of American Political Life, University of Hartford.

1920 ELECTION
Warren G. Harding and Calvin Coolidge (Republican).
Cloth beanie (hat).
Bridwell Library Special Collections.

1921 INAUGURATION
Warren G. Harding (Republican).
Official silver inaugural medal.
Bridwell Library, The Hervey A. Priddy Collection.

1923 INAUGURATION
Calvin Coolidge (Republican).

Bronze inaugural medal.
Bridwell Library, The Hervey A. Priddy Collection.

1925 INAUGURATION
Calvin Coolidge (Republican).
Official bronze inaugural medal.
Bridwell Library, The Hervey A. Priddy Collection.

1928 ELECTION
Alfred E. Smith (Democratic).
Cardboard license plate attachment.
Bridwell Library Special Collections.

1928 ELECTION
Alfred E. Smith (Democratic).
Ceramic toby mug.
Loan from the Smithsonian Institution, National Museum of American History, Behring Center.

1928 ELECTION
Herbert C. Hoover (Republican).
Ceramic toby mug.
Loan from the Smithsonian Institution, National Museum of American History, Behring Center.

1929 INAUGURATION
Herbert C. Hoover (Republican).
Official bronze inaugural medal.
Bridwell Library, The Hervey A. Priddy Collection.

1932 ELECTION
Franklin D. Roosevelt (Democratic).
Tibby Young and Rummy Davis, *The Girl I Love Is a Democrat.*
Cambridge, Mass.: Intercollegiate League, 1932.
Loan from the Smithsonian Institution, National Museum of American History, Behring Center.

1932 ELECTION
Franklin D. Roosevelt (Democratic).
"Roosevelt" lithographed pin-back button, 1932.
Bridwell Library, The Hervey A. Priddy Collection.

1932 ELECTION
Franklin D. Roosevelt (Democratic).
Portrait lithographed pin-back button.
Bridwell Library, The Hervey A. Priddy Collection.

1932 ELECTION
Franklin D. Roosevelt (Democratic).
"Labor's Choice" lithographed pin-back button.
Bridwell Library, The Hervey A. Priddy Collection.

1932 ELECTION
Franklin D. Roosevelt (Democratic).
"A Gallant Leader" lithographed pin-back button.
Bridwell Library, The Hervey A. Priddy Collection.

1932 ELECTION
Franklin D. Roosevelt (Democratic).
"Independent Voter" lithographed pin-back button.
Bridwell Library, The Hervey A. Priddy Collection.

1932 ELECTION
Franklin D. Roosevelt (Democratic).
"FDR" lithographed pin-back button.
Bridwell Library, The Hervey A. Priddy Collection.

1932 and 1936 ELECTIONS
Franklin D. Roosevelt and John N. Garner
(Democratic).
Bronze lapel medalet.
Bridwell Library, The Hervey A. Priddy Collection.

1933 INAUGURATION
Franklin D. Roosevelt (Democratic).
Official silver inaugural medal.
Bridwell Library, The Hervey A. Priddy Collection.

1933 INAUGURATION
Franklin D. Roosevelt (Democratic).
Crystal engraved inaugural goblet.
Loan from the Museum of American Political Life,
University of Hartford.

1936 ELECTION
Franklin D. Roosevelt and John N. Garner
(Democratic).
Jugate lithographed pin-back button.
Bridwell Library, The Hervey A. Priddy Collection.

1937 INAUGURATION
Franklin D. Roosevelt and John N. Garner
(Democratic).
Official bronze inaugural medal.
Bridwell Library, The Hervey A. Priddy Collection.

1937 INAUGURATION
Franklin D. Roosevelt and John N. Garner
(Democratic).
Silver-plated inaugural police badge.
Bridwell Library, The Hervey A. Priddy Collection.

1940 ELECTION
Wendell Willkie (Republican).
"Willkie for President" lithographed pin-back button.
Loan from Dr. Sandra Craig.

1940 ELECTION
Wendell Willkie (Republican).
"No Third Term" lithographed pin-back button.
Loan from Dr. Sandra Craig.

1940 ELECTION
Wendell Willkie (Republican).
"Life Begins in '40" cardboard license plate
attachment.
Loan from the Smithsonian Institution, National
Museum of American History, Behring Center.

1941 INAUGURATION
Franklin D. Roosevelt (Democratic).
Official bronze inaugural medal.
Bridwell Library, The Hervey A. Priddy Collection.

1941 INAUGURATION
Franklin D. Roosevelt (Democratic).
Official bronze "Type 2" inaugural medal.
Bridwell Library, The Hervey A. Priddy Collection.

1941 SENATE ELECTION
Franklin D. Roosevelt and Lyndon B. Johnson
(Democratic).
"This Is Not A Bomb" leaflet.
Bridwell Library, The Hervey A. Priddy Collection.

1941 SENATE ELECTION
Franklin D. Roosevelt and Lyndon B. Johnson
(Democratic).
"Me and Roosevelt for Johnson" jugate lithographed
pin-back button.
Bridwell Library, The Hervey A. Priddy Collection.

1944 ELECTION
Thomas E. Dewey (Republican).
"Vote for Dewey/Kill the Klan" poster.
Bridwell Library, The Hervey A. Priddy Collection.

1944 ELECTION
Franklin D. Roosevelt and Harry S Truman
(Democratic).
Jugate lithographed pin-back button.
Bridwell Library, The Hervey A. Priddy Collection.

1945 INAUGURATION
Franklin D. Roosevelt (Democratic).
Official bronze inaugural medal.
Bridwell Library, The Hervey A. Priddy Collection.

1945
Harry S Truman.
Typewritten letter signed to James M. Pendergast
with autographed postscript.
Washington D. C., 12 April 1945.
Loan from the Harlan Crow Library, Dallas, Texas.

1945 INAUGURATION
Harry S Truman (Democratic).
Bronze inaugural medal.
Bridwell Library, The Hervey A. Priddy Collection.

1948 ELECTION
Thomas E. Dewey (Republican).
"Dewey For President" lithographed pin-back
button.
Bridwell Library Special Collections.

1948 ELECTION
Thomas E. Dewey and Earl Warren
(Republican).
"Dewey/Warren" lithographed pin-back button.
Bridwell Library Special Collections.

1948 ELECTION
Dr. John Maxwell and Symon Gould
(Vegetarian).
"Vegetarian Party" lithographed pin-back button.
Bridwell Library Special Collections.

1948 ELECTION
Harry S Truman (Democratic).
The Story of Harry Truman (comic book).
Bridwell Library Special Collections.

1948 ELECTION
J. Strom Thurmond and Fielding L. Wright
(States' Rights Democratic).
"States' Rights Democrats" postcard.
Bridwell Library Special Collections.

1949 INAUGURATION
Harry S Truman (Democratic).
Official bronze inaugural medal.
Bridwell Library, The Hervey A. Priddy Collection.

1952 ELECTION
Dwight D. Eisenhower (Republican).
"I like IKE" earrings.
Loan from Dr. Sandra Craig.

1952 ELECTION
Dwight D. Eisenhower and Richard M. Nixon
(Republican).
"I work for Ike and Dick" lithographed pin-back
button.
Loan from Dr. Sandra Craig.

1952 ELECTION
Dwight D. Eisenhower (Republican).
"I like IKE" elephant pendant.
Loan from Dr. Sandra Craig.

1952 ELECTION
Dwight D. Eisenhower (Republican).
"IKE" blue stone brooch.
Loan from Dr. Sandra Craig.

1952 ELECTION
Dwight D. Eisenhower (Republican).
"IKE" metal stitched cloth brooch.
Loan from Dr. Sandra Craig.

1952 ELECTION
Dwight D. Eisenhower (Republican).
"IKE" lapel pin.
Loan from Dr. Sandra Craig.

1952 ELECTION
Dwight D. Eisenhower (Republican).
Portrait cloth potholder.
Loan from the Smithsonian Institution, National
Museum of American History, Behring Center.

1952 ELECTION
Dwight D. Eisenhower (Republican).
"I LIKE IKE" nylon stockings.
Loan from the Museum of American Political Life,
University of Hartford.

1952 ELECTION
Dwight D. Eisenhower (Republican).
Eisenhower "I LIKE IKE" elephant toy.
Loan from the Museum of American Political Life,
University of Hartford.

1952 ELECTION
Dwight D. Eisenhower (Republican).
"I LIKE IKE" telephone compact.
Bridwell Library Special Collections.

1953 INAUGURATION
Dwight D. Eisenhower (Republican).
Official bronze inaugural medal.
Bridwell Library, The Hervey A. Priddy Collection.

1956 ELECTION
Adlai E. Stevenson and Estes Kefauver (Democratic).
Hole-in-shoe and coonskin lapel stud.
Bridwell Library, The Hervey A. Priddy Collection.

1957 INAUGURATION
Dwight D. Eisenhower and Richard M. Nixon
(Republican).
Official bronze inaugural medal.
Bridwell Library, The Hervey A. Priddy Collection.

1960 ELECTION
John F. Kennedy (Democratic).
Autographed letter to [Robert Troutman, Jr.?].
c. 1960.
Loan from the Harlan Crow Library, Dallas, Texas.

1960 ELECTION
John F. Kennedy (Democratic).
Typewritten speech and related notes with auto-
graph revisions and notes.
Fort Worth, Texas, 13 September 1960.
Loan from the Harlan Crow Library, Dallas, Texas.

1960 ELECTION
Lyndon Johnson (Democratic).
Typewritten letter signed to Dan Ferguson.
Washington, D.C., 22 October 1960.
Bridwell Library, The Collection of Mr. and Mrs.
Dan Ferguson.

1960 ELECTION
John F. Kennedy (Democratic).
"Kennedy for President" plastic skimmer.
Loan from the Smithsonian Institution, National
Museum of American History, Behring Center.

1961 INAUGURATION
John F. Kennedy (Democratic).
Official bronze inaugural medal.
Bridwell Library, The Hervey A. Priddy Collection.

1961 INAUGURATION
John F. Kennedy and Lyndon B. Johnson
(Democratic).
Official bronze inaugural medal.
Bridwell Library, The Hervey A. Priddy Collection.

1963 INAUGURATION
Lyndon B. Johnson (Democratic).
Bronze inaugural medal.
Bridwell Library, The Hervey A. Priddy Collection.

1964 ELECTION
Margaret Chase Smith (Republican).
Flower design lithographed pin-back button.
Bridwell Library Special Collections.

1964 ELECTION
Barry Goldwater (Republican).
"Au-H2O-64" automobile bumper sticker.
Loan from the Museum of American Political Life,
University of Hartford.

1964 ELECTION
George Wallace (American Independent).
"Wallace in '68" matchbooks.
Bridwell Library, The Hervey A. Priddy Collection.

1964 ELECTION
Lyndon B. Johnson and Hubert H. Humphrey
(Democratic).
"LBJ/HHH/For the USA" matchbooks.
Bridwell Library, The Hervey A. Priddy Collection.

1964 ELECTION
Barry Goldwater (Republican).
Senator Goldwater Speaks Out on the Issues
(booklet).
Bridwell Library Special Collections.

1965 INAUGURATION
Lyndon B. Johnson (Democratic).
Official bronze inaugural medal.
Bridwell Library, The Hervey A. Priddy Collection.

1968 ELECTION
Richard M. Nixon (Republican).
"Nixon Now" lithographed pin-back button.
Bridwell Library Special Collections.

1968 ELECTION
Robert F. Kennedy (Democratic).

"For President" lithographed pin-back button.
Loan from Thomas J. Knock.

1968 ELECTION
Hubert H. Humphrey (Democratic).
"H-H-Humphrey" lithographed pin-back button.
Bridwell Library Special Collections.

1968 ELECTION
George C. Wallace (American Independent).
"Stand Up for America" metal license plate attachment.
Loan from the Smithsonian Institution, National Museum of American History, Behring Center.

1969 INAUGURATION
Richard M. Nixon (Republican).
Official bronze inaugural medal.
Bridwell Library, The Hervey A. Priddy Collection.

1972 ELECTION
George McGovern and R. Sargent Shriver (Democratic).
"Come Home America" jugate lithographed pin-back button.
Loan from Thomas J. Knock.

1972 ELECTION
George McGovern (Democratic).
Collage poster.
Loan from Thomas J. Knock.

1972 ELECTION
Dr. Spock (People's).
"People's Party" lithographed pin-back button.
Bridwell Library Special Collections.

1973 INAUGURATION
Richard M. Nixon and Spiro Agnew (Republican).
Official bronze inaugural medal.
Bridwell Library, The Hervey A. Priddy Collection.

1973 INAUGURATION
Gerald R. Ford (Republican).
Official bronze inaugural medal.
Bridwell Library, The Hervey A. Priddy Collection.

1974 INAUGURATION
Nelson A. Rockefeller (Republican).
Official bronze inaugural medal.
Bridwell Library, The Hervey A. Priddy Collection.

1974 INAUGURATION
Gerald R. Ford (Republican).
Official bronze inaugural medal.
Bridwell Library, The Hervey A. Priddy Collection.

1976 ELECTION
Jimmy Carter and Walter F. Mondale (Democratic).
"Grits 'n Fritz in '76" lithographed pin-back button.
Bridwell Library Special Collections.

1976 ELECTION
Jimmy Carter (Democratic).
"I'm A Democrat" cardboard license plate attachment.
Bridwell Library Special Collections.

1977 INAUGURATION
Jimmy Carter (Democratic).
Official bronze inaugural medal.
Bridwell Library, The Hervey A. Priddy Collection.

1980 ELECTION
Ronald Reagan (Republican).
"America/Reagan Country/Reagan Delegate" convention delegate badge.
Loan from the Smithsonian Institution, National Museum of American History, Behring Center.

1981 INAUGURATION
Ronald W. Reagan (Republican).
Official bronze inauguration medal.
Bridwell Library, The Hervey A. Priddy Collection.

1981 INAUGURATION
George H. Bush (Republican).
Official silver inaugural medal.
Bridwell Library, The Hervey A. Priddy Collection.

1984 ELECTION
Geraldine Ferraro (Democratic).
Autographed Democratic National Convention acceptance speech.
Bridwell Library Special Collections.

1984 ELECTION
Jesse L. Jackson (Rainbow Coalition).
"Win Jesse Win" lithographed pin-back button.
Bridwell Library Special Collections.

1984 ELECTION
Geraldine Ferraro (Democratic).
"Ferraro/Now! 1984" lithographed pin-back button.
Bridwell Library Special Collections.

1985 INAUGURATION
Ronald W. Reagan and George H. Bush
(Republican).
Official bronze inaugural medal.
Bridwell Library, The Hervey A. Priddy Collection.

1985 INAUGURATION
Ronald W. Reagan (Republican).
Silver-plated "Sunday" inaugural medal.
Bridwell Library, The Hervey A. Priddy Collection.

1989 INAUGURATION
George H. Bush (Republican).
Official bronze inaugural medal.
Bridwell Library, The Hervey A. Priddy Collection.

1992 ELECTION
William J. Clinton and Albert Gore, Jr.
(Democratic).
"'92/New Voice for a New America" lithographed
pin-back button.
Bridwell Library Special Collections.

1992 ELECTION
William J. Clinton and Hillary Clinton
(Democratic).
"Bill and Hillary/America's Next First Family"
lithographed pin-back button.
Bridwell Library Special Collections.

1992 ELECTION
H. Ross Perot, Sr. (Independent).
"NAFTA's Trade Deficit" chart.
Loan from the collection of H. Ross Perot, Sr.

1992 ELECTION
H. Ross Perot, Sr. (Independent).
"Federal Deficit" chart.
Loan from the collection of H. Ross Perot, Sr.

1992 ELECTION
George H. Bush and Dan Quayle (Republican).
"Christians for Bush-Quayle" lithographed
pin-back button.
Bridwell Library Special Collections.

1993 INAUGURATION
William J. Clinton and Albert Gore, Jr.
(Democratic).
Official bronze inaugural medal.
Bridwell Library, The Hervey A. Priddy Collection.

1996 ELECTION
H. Ross Perot, Sr. (Reform Party).
"Reform Party" poster.
Loan from the collection of H. Ross Perot, Sr.

1996 ELECTION
Lyndon LaRouche (Democratic).
"Give Newt the Boot" lithographed pin-back button.
Bridwell Library Special Collections.

1996 ELECTION
Robert Dole and Jack Kemp (Republican).
"We Will Fight Crime" lithographed pin-back button.
Bridwell Library Special Collections.

1997 INAUGURATION
William J. Clinton and Albert Gore, Jr.
(Democratic).
Official bronze inaugural medal.
Bridwell Library, The Hervey A. Priddy Collection.

2000 ELECTION
Albert Gore, Jr. (Democratic).
"Gore 2000/Earth in the Balance" lithographed
pin-back button.
Bridwell Library Special Collections.

2000 ELECTION
Albert Gore, Jr. (Democratic).
"I am the NEA" poster.
Bridwell Library Special Collections.

2000 ELECTION
Albert Gore, Jr. and Joseph Lieberman
(Democratic).
"Chutzpah!" lithographed pin-back button.
Bridwell Library Special Collections.

2000 ELECTION
George H. Bush and George W. Bush
(Republican).
"George to George to George" lithographed
pin-back button.
Bridwell Library Special Collections.

2000 ELECTION
George W. Bush and Dick Cheney
(Republican).
"GOP" lithographed pin-back button.
Bridwell Library, The Hervey A. Priddy Collection.

2000 ELECTION
George W. Bush (Republican).
Texas Ranger badge-shaped lapel badge.
Bridwell Library, The Hervey A. Priddy Collection.

2000 POST-ELECTION CAMPAIGN
Hillsborough County, Florida "Hanging Chad"
ballot.
Bridwell Library Special Collections.

2000 POST-ELECTION CAMPAIGN
George W. Bush (Republican).
"Sore Loserman" t-shirt.
Bridwell Library Special Collections.

2000 POST-ELECTION CAMPAIGN
Albert Gore, Jr. (Democratic).
"having my brother rig the election...priceless"
t-shirt.
Bridwell Library Special Collections.

2001 INAUGURATION
George W. Bush (Republican).
Official silver inaugural medal.
Bridwell Library, The Hervey A. Priddy Collection.

Glossary

AMBROTYPE: A photographic process developed in the mid-1850s in which a glass negative was made positive by coating its back with black paint or lacquer. Though not as detailed or sharp as a daguerreotype, the ambrotype was far less expensive. The drawback was its fragility; if the glass broke, the image was lost. By the mid-1860s, the tintype had replaced the ambrotype.

BRASS ENCASED FERROTYPE: A small photograph on metal of a candidate, usually a tintype, encased in a metal shell or frame. This was a popular campaign device from 1860 to 1880. Ferrotypes were made on large sheet iron plates, with multiple images of the candidate reproduced in the tintype process. The images were then cut out and mounted in frames.

CELLULOID: A button made by printing a design on a piece of paper, then covering the paper with a clear synthetic substance called celluloid. The image was then attached to a metal pin-back button. It was first used in the nineteenth century, but when celluloid was banned for environmental reasons in the mid-twentieth century, it was replaced by a form of acetate. Nonetheless, the buttons are still called celluloids.

COLLET: The metal ring on the back of a button that is used to hold the celluloid/acetate and paper in place.

CURL: The edge of a celluloid button, often where the manufacturer's name and a union bug appears.

DAGUERREOTYPE: A photograph on a silver-coated copper plate. The process was developed in France in the 1830s and was popular in America from 1840 to 1860.

FLASHER: A dual-image button popular in the 1960s.

JUGATE: Any campaign item picturing two candidates, usually the presidential and vice-presidential candidates of a party. Not only buttons, but also tokens, postcards, pamphlets, adhesive stamps, and other items may be called jugates.

LITHO or LITHOGRAPH: A pin-back button, often made of tin, that has its design painted or printed directly on the metal. Lithos are inexpensive to make and are a popular form of campaign button. They typically have rather simple designs.

MECHANICAL: A pin-back with moveable parts, often spring-loaded; popular around 1900.

MEDALET: A small medal about the size of a coin, bearing the likeness of a candidate on one side and a sometimes a slogan or other image on the obverse. Very popular as a campaign item during the nineteenth century.

PARADE TORCH: A kerosene lantern mounted on a pole and carried in parades during the nineteenth century; often decorated with candidates' names or slogans.

PIN-BACK: Any campaign device that is worn on the lapel by means of a clasp or pin at the back of the device.

RIBBON: A small piece of fabric, usually made of silk, with a printed or embroidered slogan or image of a candidate. Designed to be worn on the lapel.

RIBBON BADGE: A lapel device, often worn at conventions, consisting of a metal top bar from which hangs a ribbon, medal, or combination of ornaments.

SHELL BADGE: A lapel device stamped from a thin brass sheet with an embossed likeness of a candidate. This process was also used to make frames for ferrotypes and cardboard photographs.

SONGSTER: A pamphlet containing lyrics and music to campaign songs.

STICKPIN: A long vertical pin topped with a metal ornament or flag, popular around 1900.

TINTYPE: A cheap and simple way of producing photographs using wet collodion on thin black painted sheet iron (not tin). Fast and easy to produce, they needed no special care and could be put into buttons or frames for campaign buttons.

TRIGATE: Any campaign item picturing three candidates.

UNION BUG: The name of the producer printed on the curl of a button.

WHITE METAL: Also called "pot metal," it is an alloy of lead and tin and was often used for casting trinkets in the nineteenth century.

WINDOW STICKER: A graphic paper sign designed to be moistened with water and applied to glass. A popular campaign item—for automobile windows—from the 1920s to the mid-twentieth century.

American Presidential Candidates, 1789–2000

1789

George Washington	*(No party designations)*
John Adams	
John Jay	
Robert H. Harrison	
John Rutledge	
John Hancock	
George Clinton	
Samuel Huntington	
John Milton	
James Armstrong	
Edward Telfair	
Benjamin Lincoln	

1792

George Washington	*(No party designations)*
John Adams	
George Clinton	
Thomas Jefferson	
Aaron Burr	

1796

John Adams	*Federalist*
Thomas Jefferson	*Democratic-Republican*
Thomas Pinckney	*Federalist*
Aaron Burr	*Democratic-Republican*
Samuel Adams	*Democratic-Republican*
Oliver Ellsworth	*Federalist*
George Clinton	*Democratic-Republican*

John Jay	*Federalist*
James Iredell	*Federalist*
Samuel Johnston	*Federalist*
George Washington	*Federalist*
John Henry	*Federalist*
Charles C. Pinckney	*Federalist*

1800

Thomas Jefferson	*Democratic-Republican*
Aaron Burr	*Democratic-Republican*
John Adams	*Federalist*
Charles C. Pinckney	*Federalist*
John Jay	*Federalist*

1804

Thomas Jefferson	*Democratic-Republican*
Charles C. Pinckney	*Federalist*

1808

James Madison	*Democratic-Republican*
Charles C. Pinckney	*Federalist*
George Clinton	*Democratic-Republican*

1812

James Madison	*Democratic-Republican*
DeWitt Clinton	*Federalist*

1816

James Monroe	*Democratic-Republican*
Rufus King	*Federalist*

1820
James Monroe — *Democratic-Republican*
John Q. Adams — *Independent-Republican*

1824
John Q. Adams — *Democratic-Republican*
Andrew Jackson — *Democratic-Republican*
William H. Crawford — *Democratic-Republican*
Henry Clay — *Democratic-Republican*

1828
Andrew Jackson — *Democratic*
John Q. Adams — *National Republican*

1832
Andrew Jackson — *Democratic*
Henry Clay — *National Republican*
John Floyd — *Independent Democrats*
William Wirt — *Anti-Masonic*

1836
Martin Van Buren — *Democratic*
William H. Harrison — *Anti-Masonic/Whig*
Hugh L. White — *Whig*
Daniel Webster — *Whig*
W. P. Mangum — *Independent/Whig*

1840
William H. Harrison — *Whig*
Martin Van Buren — *Democratic*
James G. Birney — *Liberty (Prohibition)*

1844
James K. Polk — *Democratic*
Henry Clay — *Whig*
James G. Birney — *Liberty (Prohibition)*

1848
Zachary Taylor — *Whig*
Lewis Cass — *Democratic*
Martin Van Buren — *Free Soil (Democrat)*
Gerrit Smith — *National Liberty/ Liberty League*

1852
Franklin Pierce — *Democratic*
Winfield Scott — *Whig*
John P. Hale — *Free Soil (Democrat)*
Daniel Webster — *Whig*
George M. Troop — *Southern Rights*
Gerrit Smith — *National Liberty*

1856
James Buchanan — *Democratic*
John C. Frémont — *Republican*
Millard Fillmore — *American (Know-Nothing)/ Whig*
Gerrit Smith — *Land Reform*

1860
Abraham Lincoln — *Republican*
John C. Breckinridge — *Southern Democratic*
John Bell — *Constitutional Union*
Stephen A. Douglas — *Democratic*

1864
Abraham Lincoln — *Union (Republican)*
George B. McClellan — *Democratic*

1868
Ulysses S. Grant — *Republican*
Horatio Seymour — *Democratic*

1872
Ulysses S. Grant — *Republican*
Horace Greeley — *Democratic/Liberal Republican*
Thomas A. Hendricks — *Independent Democrat*
B. Gratz Brown — *Democratic*
Charles J. Jenkins — *Democratic*
David Davis — *Democratic*
Charles O'Conor — *"Straight-Out" Democrat*
James Black — *National Prohibition*
Victoria C. Woodhull — *People's/Equal Rights*
William S. Groesbeck — *Independent Liberal Republican*

1876
Rutherford B. Hayes — *Republican*
Samuel J. Tilden — *Democratic*
Peter Cooper — *National Independent (Greenback)*
Green C. Smith — *Prohibition*
James B. Walker — *American National*

1880
James Garfield — *Republican*
Winfield S. Hancock — *Democratic*
James B. Weaver — *Greenback-Labor*
Neal Dow — *Prohibition*
John W. Phelps — *American/Anti-Masonic*

1884

Grover Cleveland	*Democratic*
James G. Blaine	*Republican*
Benjamin F. Butler	*Greenback-Labor*
John P. St. John	*Prohibition*
Belva Ann Lockwood	*Equal Rights*
Peter D. Wigginton	*American*
Samuel C. Pomeroy	*American Prohibition National*

1888

Benjamin Harrison	*Republican*
Grover Cleveland	*Democratic*
Clinton B. Fisk	*Prohibition*
Anson J. Streeter	*Union Labor*
Robert H. Cowdrey	*United Labor*
James L. Curtis	*American*
Belva Ann Lockwood	*Equal Rights*
Albert Redstone	*Industrial Reform*

1892

Grover Cleveland	*Democratic*
Benjamin Harrison	*Republican*
James B. Weaver	*People's (Populist)*
John Bidwell	*Prohibition*
Simon Wing	*Socialist-Labor*

1896

William McKinley	*Republican*
William J. Bryan	*Democratic*
John Palmer	*National Democratic*
Joshua Levering	*Prohibition*
Charles H. Matchett	*Socialist-Labor*
Charles E. Bentley	*Nationalist*

1900

William McKinley	*Republican*
William J. Bryan	*Democratic*
John G. Woolley	*Prohibition*
Eugene V. Debs	*Social Democratic*
Wharton Barker	*People's (Populist)*
Joseph Maloney	*Socialist-Labor*
Seth H. Ellis	*Union Reform*
Jonah Leonard	*United Christian*
Job Harriman	*Social Democrat of USA*

1904

Theodore Roosevelt	*Republican*
Alton B. Parker	*Democratic*
Eugene V. Debs	*Socialist*
Silas C. Swallow	*Prohibition*
Thomas E. Watson	*People's (Populist)*
Charles H. Corregan	*Socialist-Labor*
Austin Holcomb	*Continental*
George E. Taylor	*National Liberty*

1908

William H. Taft	*Republican*
William J. Bryan	*Democratic*
Eugene V. Debs	*Socialist*
Eugene W. Chafin	*Prohibition*
Thomas L. Hisgin	*Independence*
Thomas E. Watson	*People's (Populist)*
August Gillhaus	*Socialist-Labor*
Daniel B. Turney	*United Christian*

1912

Woodrow Wilson	*Democratic*
Theodore Roosevelt	*Progressive*
William H. Taft	*Republican*
Eugene V. Debs	*Socialist*
Eugene W. Chafin	*Prohibition*
Arthur E. Reimer	*Socialist-Labor*

1916

Woodrow Wilson	*Democratic*
Charles E. Hughes	*Republican*
Allen L. Benson	*Socialist*
James F. Hanly	*Prohibition*
Theodore Roosevelt	*Progressive*
Arthur E. Reimer	*Socialist-Labor*
William Sulzer	*American*

1920

Warren G. Harding	*Republican*
James M. Cox	*Democratic*
Eugene V. Debs	*Socialist*
Parley Christensen	*Farmer-Labor*
Aaron S. Watkins	*Prohibition*
James E. Ferguson	*American*
W. W. Cox	*Socialist-Labor*
Robert C. MacCauley	*Single Tax*

1924

Calvin Coolidge	*Republican*
John W. Davis	*Democratic*
Robert M. La Follette	*Progressive*
Herman P. Faris	*Prohibition*
Frank T. Johns	*Socialist-Labor*

William Z. Foster   *Worker's (Communist)*
Gilbert O. Nations   *American*
William J. Wallace   *Commonwealth Land*
John Zahnd   *National Independent*
                         (Greenback)
Jacob Coxey   *Farmer-Labor*

1928

Herbert C. Hoover   *Republican*
Alfred E. Smith   *Democratic*
Norman Thomas   *Socialist*
William Z. Foster   *Worker's (Communist)*
Verne L. Reynolds   *Socialist-Labor*
William F. Varney   *Prohibition*
Frank E. Webb   *Farmer-Labor*
John Zahnd   *National Independent*
                         (Greenback)

1932

Franklin D. Roosevelt   *Democratic*
Herbert C. Hoover   *Republican*
Norman Thomas   *Socialist*
William Z. Foster   *Worker's (Communist)*
William D. Upshaw   *Prohibition*
William H. Harvey   *Liberty*
Verne L. Reynolds   *Socialist-Labor*
Jacob Coxey   *Farmer-Labor*
John Zahnd   *National Independent*
                         (Greenback)
James R. Cox   *Jobless*

1936

Franklin D. Roosevelt   *Democratic*
Alfred M. Landon   *Republican*
William Lemke   *National Union*
Norman Thomas   *Socialist*
Earl R. Browder   *Communist*
David L. Colvin   *Prohibition/National*
                         Prohibition/Commonwealth
John W. Aiken   *Socialist-Labor*
William D. Pelley   *Christian*
John Zahnd   *National Independent*
                         (Greenback)

1940

Franklin D. Roosevelt   *Democratic*
Wendell L. Willkie   *Republican*
Norman Thomas   *Socialist*
Roger W. Babson   *Prohibition*

Earl Browder   *Communist*
John W. Aiken   *Socialist-Labor*
Alfred Knutson   *Independent*
John Zahnd   *National Independent*
                         (Greenback)
Anna Milburn   *National Greenback*

1944

Franklin D. Roosevelt   *Democratic*
Thomas E. Dewey   *Republican*
Norman Thomas   *Socialist*
Claude Watson   *Prohibition*
Edward Teichert   *Socialist-Labor*
Harry F. Byrd   *Southern Democrats*
Gerald L. K. Smith   *America First*

1948

Harry S Truman   *Democratic*
Thomas E. Dewey   *Republican*
J. Strom Thurmond   *States' Rights Democratic*
Henry A. Wallace   *Progressive*
Norman Thomas   *Socialist*
Claude A. Watson   *Prohibition*
Edward Teichert   *Socialist-Labor*
Farrell Dobbs   *Socialist Workers/Militant*
                         Workers
Gerald L. K. Smith   *Christian Nationalist*
                         Crusade
John G. Scott   *Greenback*
John Maxwell   *Vegetarian*

1952

Dwight D. Eisenhower   *Republican*
Adlai E. Stevenson   *Democratic*
Vincent W. Halliman   *Progressive/American Labor*
Stuart Hamblen   *Prohibition*
Eric Hass   *Socialist-Labor*
Darlington Hoopes   *Socialist*
Douglas A. MacArthur   *America First*
Farrell Dobbs   *Socialist Workers/Militant*
                         Workers
Henry B. Krajewski   *Poor Man's Party*
Homer A. Tomlinson   *Church of God Bible*
                         Party
Frederick C. Proehl   *Greenback*
Ellen L. Jensen   *Washington Peace*
Daniel J. Murphy   *American Vegetarian*

1956

Dwight D. Eisenhower	*Republican*
Adlai E. Stevenson	*Democratic*
Walter B. Jones	*No party*
T. Coleman Andrews	*Independent States' Rights*
Harry F. Byrd	*Independent*
Eric Hass	*Socialist-Labor*
Enoch A. Holtwick	*Prohibition*
William E. Jenner	*Texas Constitution*
Farrell Dobbs	*Socialist Workers/ Militant Workers*
Darlington Hoopes	*Socialist*
Henry B. Krajewski	*American Third Party*
Gerald L. K. Smith	*Christian National*
Homer A. Tomlinson	*Theocratic*
Herbert M. Shelton	*American Vegetarian*
Frederick C. Proehl	*Greenback*
William Langer	*Pioneer*

1960

John F. Kennedy	*Democratic*
Richard M. Nixon	*Republican*
Harry F. Byrd	*Independent*
Orval Faubus	*States' Rights*
Eric Hass	*Socialist-Labor*
Rutherford L. Decker	*Prohibition*
Farrell Dobbs	*Socialist Workers*
Charles L. Sullivan	*Texas Constitution*
Joseph B. Lee	*Conservative Party of New Jersey*
C. Benton Coiner	*Conservative Party of Virginia*
Lar Daly	*Tax Cut*
Clennon King	*Afro-American*
Merrit B. Curtis	*Independent/ Constitution*
Symon Gould	*American Vegetarian*
Whitney H. Slocum	*Greenback*
Homer A. Tomlinson	*Theocratic*

1964

Lyndon B. Johnson	*Democratic*
Barry M. Goldwater	*Republican*
Eric Hass	*Socialist-Labor*
Clifton DeBerry	*Socialist Workers*
Earle H. Munn	*Prohibition*
John Kaspar	*National States' Rights*

Joseph B. Lightburn	*Constitution*
Kirby J. Hensley	*Universal*
Homer A. Tomlinson	*Theocratic*
T. Coleman Andrews	*Independent States' Rights*
Yette Bronstein	*Best Party*
D. X. B. Schwartz	*National Tax Savers*
Louis E. Jaeckel	*American*

1968

Richard M. Nixon	*Republican*
Hubert H. Humphrey	*Democratic*
George C. Wallace	*American Independent*
Henning A. Blomen	*Socialist-Labor*
Dick Gregory	*Various parties*
Fred Halstead	*Socialist Workers*
Eldridge Cleaver	*Peace and Freedom*
Eugene McCarthy	*New Party*
Earle H. Munn	*Prohibition*
Charlene Mitchell	*Communist*

1972

Richard M. Nixon	*Republican*
George S. McGovern	*Democratic*
John G. Schmitz	*American*
Linda Jenness	*Socialist Workers*
Louis Fisher	*Socialist-Labor*
Gus Hall	*Communist*
Earle H. Munn	*Prohibition*
Joseph Hospers	*Libertarian*

1976

Jimmy Carter	*Democratic*
Gerald Ford	*Republican*
Eugene McCarthy	*Independent*
Roger L. MacBride	*Libertarian*
Lester G. Maddox	*American Independent*
Thomas J. Anderson	*American*
Peter Camejo	*Socialist Workers*
Gus Hall	*Communist*
Margaret Wright	*People's*
Lyndon H. LaRouche	*U.S. Labor*
Benjamin Bubar	*Prohibition*
Jules Levin	*Socialist-Labor*
Frank P. Zeidler	*Socialist*

1980

Ronald Reagan	*Republican*
Jimmy Carter	*Democratic*

John B. Anderson	*Independent*
Ed Clark	*Libertarian*
Barry Commoner	*Citizens*
Clifton DeBerry	*Socialist Workers*
Gus Hall	*Communist*
John R. Rarick	*American Independent*
Ellen McCormack	*Independent*
Maureen Smith	*Peace and Freedom*
Percy L. Greaves	*American*
Deidre Griswold	*Workers World*
Benjamin Bubar	*National Statesman*
David McReynolds	*Socialist*
Kurt Lynen	*Middle Class*
Bill Gahres	*Down With Lawyers*
Martin Wendelken	*Independent*
Harley McLain	*Natural People's League*

1984

Ronald Reagan	*Republican*
Walter F. Mondale	*Democratic*
David Bergland	*Libertarian*
Lyndon H. LaRouche	*Independent Democrat*
Sonia Johnson	*Citizens*
Bob Richards	*Populist*
Dennis Serrette	*Independent Alliance*
Gus Hall	*Communist*
Mel Mason	*Socialist Workers*
Larry Holmes	*Workers World*
Delmar Davis	*American*
Ed Winn	*Workers League*
Earl F. Dodge	*National Statesman*
John D. Anderson	*National Unity Party of Kentucky*

1988

George H. Bush	*Republican*
Michael S. Dukakis	*Democratic*
Ron Paul	*Libertarian*
Lenora B. Fulani	*New Alliance*
David E. Duke	*Independent Populist*
Eugene J. McCarthy	*Consumer*
Warren Griffin	*American Independent*
Lyndon H. LaRouche	*Independent*
William Marra	*Right to Life*
Ed Winn	*Workers League*
James Mac Warren	*Socialist Workers*
Herbert Lewin	*Peace and Freedom*
Earl F. Dodge	*National Statesman*

Larry Holmes	*Workers World*
Willa Kenoyer	*Socialist*
Delmar Dennis	*American*
Jack Herer	*Grassroots*
Louie G. Youngkeit	*Independent*
John G. Martin	*Third World Assembly*

1992

William J. Clinton	*Democratic*
George H. Bush	*Republican*
H. Ross Perot, Sr.	*Independent Reform*
Andre V. Marrou	*Libertarian*
James Gritz	*Populist*
Lenora B. Fulani	*New Alliance*
Howard Phillips	*U.S. Taxpayers*
John Hagelin	*Natural Law*
Ronald Daniels	*Peace and Freedom*
Lyndon H. LaRouche	*Economic Recovery*
James Warren	*Socialist Workers*

1996

William J. Clinton	*Democratic*
Robert Dole	*Republican*
H. Ross Perot, Sr.	*Independent Reform*
Ralph Nader	*Green*
Harry Browne	*Libertarian*
Howard Phillips	*U.S. Taxpayers*
John Hagelin	*Natural Law*
Monica Moorehead	*Workers World*
Marsha Feinland	*Peace and Freedom*
James Harris	*Socialist Workers*

2000

George W. Bush	*Republican*
Albert Gore, Jr.	*Democratic*
Ralph Nader	*Green*
Patrick Buchanon	*Reform*
Harry Browne	*Libertarian*
Howard Phillips	*Constitution*
James Harris	*Socialist Workers*
Neil Smith	*Arizona Libertarian*
David McReynolds	*Socialist*

ITEM 25
Women's Suffrage
pin-back buttons,
c. 1900.

Bibliography

Adams, Charles Francis, ed. *Memoirs of John Quincy Adams, Comprising Portions of His Diary from 1795 to 1848.* 12 vols. Philadelphia: J. B. Lippincott & Co., 1874-1877.

Adams, Samuel Hopkins. *Incredible Era: The Life and Times of Warren Gamaliel Harding.* Boston: Houghton Mifflin, 1939.

Addams, Jane. *Twenty Years at Hull-House, with Autobiographical Notes.* New York: The MacMillan Co., 1910.

Altschuler, Glenn C. *Rude Republic: Americans and Their Politics in the Nineteenth Century.* Princeton, N.J.: Princeton University Press, 2000.

Ansolabehere, Stephen, and Shanto Iyengar. *Going Negative: How Attack Ads Shrink and Polarize the Electorate.* New York: The Free Press, 1995.

Bailey, Michael A., Ronald A. Faucheux, Paul S. Herrnson, and Clyde Wilcox, eds. *Campaigns & Elections: Contemporary Case Studies.* Washington, D.C.: Congressional Quarterly, Inc., 2000.

Baker, Paula. "The Domestication of Politics: Women and American Political Society, 1789–1920." *American Historical Review* 89 (June 1984): 620-47.

Baker, Paula. *The Moral Framework of Public Life: Gender, Politics, and the State in Rural New York, 1870-1930.* New York: Oxford University Press, 1991.

Baum, Dale. *The Civil War Party System: The Case of Massachusetts, 1848-1876.* Chapel Hill: University of North Carolina Press, 1984.

Benson, Lee. *The Concept of Jacksonian Democracy: New York as a Test Case.* Princeton, N.J.: Princeton University Press, 1961.

Benson, Lee, and Joel H. Silbey. "Toward a Theory of Stability and Change in American Voting Patterns: New York State, 1792-1970," in Joel H. Silbey, Allan G. Bogue, and William H. Flanigan, eds. *The History of American Electoral Behavior.* Princeton, N.J.: Princeton University Press, 1978, pp. 78-105.

Beveridge, Albert J. *Abraham Lincoln: 1809-1858.* Boston & New York: Houghton Mifflin Company, 1928.

Biocca, Frank, ed. *Television and Political Advertising, Volume 1: Psychological Processes.* Hillsdale, N.J.: Lawrence Earlbaum Associates, 1991.

Bishop, Joseph Bucklin. *Presidential Nominations and Elections: A History of American Conventions and National Campaigns, Inaugurations and Campaign Caricature.* New York: Charles Scribner's Sons, 1916.

Blaine, James Gillespie. *Twenty Years of Congress, from Lincoln to Garfield, with a Review of the Events which Led to the Political Revolution of 1860.* 2 vols. Norwich, Conn.: The Henry Bill Publishing Co., 1884-1886.

Bonomi, Patricia U., ed. *Party and Political Opposition in Revolutionary America.* Tarrytown, N.Y.: Sleepy Hollow Press, 1980.

Brady, David W. and Matthew D. McCubbins. *Party, Process, and Political Change in Congress: New Perspectives on the History of Congress.* Stanford, Calif.: Stanford University Press, 2002.

Breckinridge, Sophonisba. *Women in the Twentieth Century: A Study of Their Political, Social, and Economic Activities.* New York: McGraw Hill, 1933.

Burnham, Walter Dean. *Critical Elections and the Mainsprings of American Politics.* New York: W. W. Norton and Company, 1970.

Burnham, Walter Dean. "Those High Nineteenth-Century American Voting Turnouts: Fact or Fiction?" *Journal of Interdisciplinary History* 16 (Spring 1985): 613-44.

Campbell, Angus, Philip E. Converse, Warren E. Miller, and Donald E. Stokes. *The American Voter.* New York: John Wiley and Sons, 1960.

Chafe, William Henry. *The American Woman: Her Changing Social, Economic, and Political Roles, 1920-1970.* New York: Oxford University Press, 1972.

Chester, Edward W. *Radio, Television, and American Politics.* New York: Sheed and Ward, 1969.

Committee for the Study of the American Electorate. *Battleground State Mobilization Efforts Propel Voter Turnout Slightly Upward in Historic but Disturbing Election,* http://www.washington-post.com/wp-rv/politics/daily/graphics/voterturnout_110802.html, "Voter Turnout."

Cooper, William J., Jr., Michael F. Holt, and John McCardell, eds. *A Master's Due: Essays in Honor of David Herbert Donald.* Baton Rouge, La.: Louisiana State University Press, 1985.

Cotler, G. "That Plague of Spots on Madison Avenue," *Reporter* (Nov. 1942).

Crotty, William. *American Parties in Decline,* 2nd ed. Boston: Little, Brown, and Company, 1984.

Crouse, Timothy. *The Boys on the Bus.* New York: Random House, 1972.

Cunliffe, Marcus. *George Washington: Man and Monument.* Boston: Little, Brown, 1958.

Cunningham, Noble E., Jr. *The Jeffersonian Republicans: The Formation of Party Organization, 1798-1801.* Chapel Hill: University of North Carolina Press, 1957.

Cunningham, Noble E., Jr. *Popular Images of the Presidency from Washington to Lincoln.* Columbia, Mo.: University of Missouri Press, 1991.

Cunningham, Noble E., Jr., ed. *The Making of the American Party System: 1789-1809.* Inglewood Cliffs, N.J.: Prentice-Hall, 1965.

Dallek, Robert. *Hail to the Chief: The Making and Unmaking of American Presidents.* New York: Hyperion, 1996.

Daniels, Walter M., ed. *Presidential Election Reforms.* New York: The H. W. Wilson Company, 1953.

De Tocqueville, Alexis. *Democracy in America.* 2 vols. New York: Everyman's Library, Alfred A. Knopf, 1994.

DeWitt, J. Doyle. *A Century of Campaign Buttons, 1789-1889.* Hartford, Conn.: The Traveler's Press, 1959.

Diamond, Edwin and Stephen Bates. *The Spot: The Rise of Political Advertising on Television.* Cambridge, Mass.: MIT Press, 1984.

Dickens, Charles. *American Notes*. Bloomsbury, England: The Nonesuch Press, 1938.

DiClerico, Robert D. *Political Parties, Campaigns, and Elections*. Upper Saddle River, N.J.: Prentice Hall, 2000.

Dionne, E. J., Jr. *Why Americans Hate Politics*. New York: Simon & Schuster, 1991.

Donald, David Herbert. *Lincoln*. New York: Simon and Schuster, 1995.

Doppelt, Jack C., and Ellen Shearer. *Nonvoters: America's No-Shows*. Thousand Oaks, Calif.: Sage Publications, 1999.

Dover, E. D. *Presidential Elections in the Television Age, 1960-1992*. Westport, Conn.: Praeger, 1994.

Dunne, Finley Peter. *Dissertations by Mr. Dooley*. Upper Saddle River, N.J.: Literature House, 1969.

Finnegan, Margaret. *Selling Suffrage: Consumer Culture and Votes for Women*. New York: Columbia University Press, 1999.

Fischel, Jeff, ed. *Parties and Elections in an Anti-Party Age: American Politics and the Crisis of Confidence*. Bloomington, Ind.: Indiana University Press, 1978.

Fischer, Roger A. *Tippecanoe and Trinkets Too: The Material Culture of Presidential Campaigns, 1828-1984*. Urbana, Ill.: University of Illinois Press, 1988.

Fischer, Roger A. and Edmund B. Sullivan. *American Political Ribbons and Ribbon Badges, 1825-1981*. Lincoln, Mass.: Quarterman Publications, Inc., 1985.

Flexner, James Thomas. *George Washington and the New Nation, 1783-1793*. Boston: Little, Brown, and Company, 1970.

Formisano, Ronald P. *The Birth of Mass Political Parties, Michigan, 1827-1861*. Princeton, N.J.: Princeton University Press, 1971.

Formisano, Ronald P. "Deferential-Participant Politics: The Early Republic's Political Culture, 1789-1840." *The American Political Science Review* 68 (June 1974): 473-87.

Formisano, Ronald P. "Ethnicity and Party in Michigan, 1854-60," in Frederick C. Luebke, ed., *Ethnic Voters and the Election of Lincoln*. Lincoln, Nebr.: University of Nebraska Press, 1971, pp. 175-94.

Formisano, Ronald P. "The Invention of the Ethnocultural Interpretation." *The American Historical Review* 99 (April 1994): 453-77.

Formisano, Ronald P. "The New Political History and the Election of 1840." *Journal of Interdisciplinary History* 23 (Spring 1993): 661-82.

Formisano, Ronald P. "Political Character, Antipartyism and the Second Party System." *American Quarterly* 21 (Winter 1969): 683-709.

Formisano, Ronald P. *The Transformation of Political Culture: Massachusetts Parties, 1790s-1840s*. New York: Oxford University Press, 1983.

Fox, Richard Wightman and T. J. Jackson Lears, eds. *The Culture of Consumption: Critical Essays in American History, 1880-1980*. New York: Pantheon Books, 1983.

Fredman, Lionel E. *The Australian Ballot: The Story of an American Reform*. East Lansing, Mich.: Michigan State University Press, 1968.

Freedom Forum Media Studies Center. *The Homestretch: New Politics. New Media. New Voters?*. New York: Columbia University Press, 1992.

Freeman, Douglas Southall. *George Washington: A Biography*, Volume Six: *Patriot and President*. New York: Charles Scribner's Sons, 1954.

Freeman, Joanne B. *Affairs of Honor: National Politics in the New Republic*. New Haven, Conn.: Yale University Press, 2001.

Genovese, Michael A. *The Power of the American Presidency, 1789-2000*. New York: Oxford University Press, 2001.

Gienapp, William E. *The Origins of the Republican Party, 1852-1856*. New York: Oxford University Press, 1987.

Gienapp, William E. "'Politics Seem to Enter Into Everything': Political Culture in the North, 1840-1860," in Stephen E. Maizlish and John G. Kushma, eds., *Essays on American Antebellum Politics, 1840-1860*. College Station, Tex.: Texas A&M University Press for the University of Texas at Arlington, 1982, pp. 15-69.

Gillespie, J. David. *Politics at the Periphery: Third Parties in Two-Party America*. Columbia, S.C.: University of South Carolina Press, 1993.

Gould, Lewis L. *Grand Old Party: A History of the Republicans*. New York: Random House, 2003.

Gould, Lewis L. *The Modern American Presidency*. Lawrence, Kans.: University Press of Kansas, 2003.

Gould, Lewis L. *The Presidency of Theodore Roosevelt*. Lawrence, Kans.: University Press of Kansas, 1991.

Gould, Lewis L. *The Presidency of William McKinley*. Lawrence, Kans.: Regents Press of Kansas, 1980.

Gould, Lewis L. "The Republican Search for a National Majority," in H. Wayne Morgan, *The Gilded Age*. Syracuse, N.Y.: Syracuse University Press, 1970, pp. 171-87.

Graham, Sara Hunter. *Woman Suffrage and the New Democracy*. New Haven, Conn.: Yale University Press, 1996.

Green, Elna C. *Southern Strategies: Southern Women and the Woman Suffrage Question*. Chapel Hill: University of North Carolina Press, 1997.

Gunderson, Robert Gray. *The Log-Cabin Campaign*. Westport, Conn.: Greenwood Press, 1957.

Gunther, John. *Taken at the Flood: The Story of Albert D. Lasker*. New York: Harper, 1960.

Gustafson, Melanie Susan. *Women and the Republican Party, 1854-1924*. Urbana, Ill.: University of Illinois Press, 2001.

Hand, Samuel B. *The Star that Set: The Vermont Republican Party, 1854-1974*. Lanham, Md.: Lexington Books, 2002.

Harvey, Anna L. *Votes Without Leverage: Women In American Electoral Politics, 1920-1970*. New York: Cambridge University Press, 1998.

Hays, Samuel P. "The Social Analysis of American Political History, 1880-1920." *Political Science Quarterly* 80 (September 1965): 373-94.

Heale, M. J. *The Making of American Politics, 1750-1850*. New York: Longman, 1977.

Heale, M. J. *The Presidential Quest: Candidates and Images in American Political Culture, 1787-1852*. New York: Longman, 1982.

Herbert S. Parmet. *Eisenhower and the American Crusades*. New York: The MacMillan Group, 1972.

Historical Statistics of the United States, from Colonial Times to 1970. Bicentennial Edition. Washington, D.C.: U.S. Department of Commerce, Bureau of Census, 1975.

Hofstadter, Richard. *The Idea of a Party System: The Rise of Legitimate Opposition in the United States, 1780-1840*. Berkeley, Calif.: University of California Press, 1969.

Holt, Michael F. *Forging a Majority: The Formation of the Republican Party in Pittsburgh, 1848-1860*. New Haven, Conn.: Yale University Press, 1969.

Holt, Michael F. *Political Parties and American Political Development from the Age of Jackson to the Age of Lincoln*. Baton Rouge, La.: Louisiana State University Press, 1992.

Holt, Michael F. *The Political Crisis of the 1850s*. New York: John Wiley, 1978.

Holt, Michael F. *The Rise and Fall of the American Whig Party: Jacksonian Politics and the Onset of the Civil War*. New York: Oxford University Press, 1999.

Irving, Washington. *Rip Van Winkle: A Legend of the Kaatskill Mountains*. New York: G. P. Putnam and Sons, 1870.

Jackson, Donald, and Dorothy Twohig, eds. *The Diaries of George Washington*. 6 vols. Charlottesville, Va.: University Press of Virginia, 1976-1979.

Jamieson, Kathleen Hall. *Dirty Politics: Deception, Distraction, and Democracy.* New York: Oxford University Press, 1992.

Jamieson, Kathleen Hall. *Packaging the Presidency: A History and Criticism of Presidential Campaign Advertising.* New York: Oxford University Press, 1984.

Jensen, Richard. "Armies, Admen, and Crusaders: Types of Presidential Election Campaigns." *The History Teacher* 2 (Jan. 1969): 33-50.

Jensen, Richard J. *Grassroots Politics: Parties, Issues, and Voters, 1854-1983.* Westport, Conn.: Greenwood Press, 1983.

Jensen, Richard J. *The Winning of the Midwest: Social and Political Conflict, 1888-1896.* Chicago: University of Chicago Press, 1971.

Johnson, Haynes. *The Best of Times: America in the Clinton Years.* New York: Harcourt, 2001.

Johnson-Cartee, Karen S., and Gary A. Copeland. *Negative Political Advertising: Coming of Age.* Hillsdale, N.J.: Lawrence Erlbaum Associates, 1991.

Joslyn, Richard. *Mass Media and Elections.* Redding, Mass.: Addison Wesley, 1984.

Julian, George Washington. *Political Recollections: 1840-1872.* Chicago: Jansen, McClurg, and Co., 1884.

Kaid, Lynda Lee, and Christina Holz-Bacha, eds. *Political Advertising in Western Democracies: Parties and Candidates on Television.* Thousand Oaks, Calif.: Sage Publications, 1995.

Kann, Mark E. *A Republic of Men: The American Founders, Gendered Language, and Patriarchal Politics.* New York: New York University Press, 1998.

Kann, Mark E. *The Gendering of American Politics: Founding Mothers, Founding Fathers, and Political Patriarchy.* Westport, Conn.: Praeger, 1999.

Karson, Marc. *American Labor Unions and Politics, 1900-1918.* Carbondale, Ill.: Southern Illinois University Press, 1958.

Keller, Morton. *Affairs of State: Public Life in Late Nineteenth Century America.* Cambridge, Mass.: Harvard University Press, 1977.

Keller, Morton. *The Art and Politics of Thomas Nast.* New York: Oxford University Press, 1968.

Kelley, Robert. "Ideology and Political Culture from Jefferson to Nixon." *American Historical Review* 82 (June 1977): 531-62.

Kerber, Linda K. *Federalists in Dissent: Imagery and Ideology in Jeffersonian America.* Ithaca, N.Y.: Cornell University Press, 1970.

Ketcham, Ralph. *Presidents Above Party: The First American Presidency, 1789-1829.* Chapel Hill: University of North Carolina Press, 1984.

Key, V. O., Jr. "A Theory of Critical Elections." *Journal of Politics* 17 (Feb. 1955): 3-18.

Key, V. O., Jr. "Secular Realignments and the Party System." *Journal of Politics* 21 (May 1959): 198-210.

Keyssar, Alexander. *The Right to Vote: The Contested History of Democracy in the United States.* New York: Basic Books, 2000.

King, Anthony, ed. *The New American Political System.* 2nd ed. Washington, D.C.: The AEI Press, 1990.

Kleppner, Paul. *Continuity and Change in Electoral Politics, 1893-1928.* New York: Greenwood Press, 1987.

Kleppner, Paul. *The Cross of Culture: A Social Analysis of Midwestern Politics, 1850-1900.* New York: Free Press, 1970.

Kleppner, Paul. "Lincoln and the Immigrant Vote: A Case of Religious Polarization," in Frederick C. Luebke, ed., *Ethnic Voters and the Election of Lincoln.* Lincoln, Neb.: University of Nebraska Press, 1971, pp. 151-74.

Kleppner, Paul. *The Third Electoral System, 1853-1892: Parties, Voters, and Political Cultures.* Chapel Hill: University of North Carolina Press, 1979.

Kleppner, Paul. *Who Voted? The Dynamics of Electoral Turnout, 1870-1980.* New York: Praeger, 1982.

Kornbluh, Mark Lawrence. *Why America Stopped Voting: The Decline of Participatory Democracy and the Emergence of Modern American Politics.* New York: New York University Press, 2000.

Kornhauser, Arthur, Harold L. Sheppard, and Albert J. Mayer. *When Labor Votes: A Study of Auto Workers.* New York: University Books, 1956.

Kousser, J. Morgan. *The Shaping of Southern Politics: Suffrage Restriction and the Establishment of the One-Party South, 1880-1910.* New Haven, Conn.: Yale University Press, 1974.

Kruschke, Earl Roger. *The Woman Voter.* Washington, D.C.: Public Affairs Press, 1955.

Ladd, Everett Carll. *Where Have All the Voters Gone?: The Fracturing of America's Political Parties.* New York: W. W. Norton & Company, 1977.

Langston, Thomas S. *With Reverence and Contempt: How Americans Think About Their President.* Baltimore, Md.: Johns Hopkins University Press, 1995.

Leuchtenburg, William E. *Franklin D. Roosevelt and the New Deal.* New York: Harper and Row, 1963.

Levy, Mark R., and Michael S. Kramer. *The Ethnic Factor: How America's Minorities Decide Elections.* New York: Simon and Schuster, 1972.

Lichtman, Allan J. "Critical Election Theory and the Reality of American Presidential Politics, 1916-1940." *American Historical Review* 81 (April 1976): 317-51.

Lichtman, Allan J. "The End of Realignment Theory? Toward a New Research Program for American Political History." *Historical Methods* 15 (Fall 1982): 170-88.

Luebke, Frederick C., ed. *Ethnic Voters and the Election of Lincoln.* Lincoln, Nebr.: University of Nebraska Press, 1971.

MacNeil, Neil. *The President's Medal, 1789-1977.* New York: Clarkson N. Potter, Inc., 1977.

Maisel, L. Sandy, and William G. Shade. *Parties and Politics in American History: A Reader.* New York: Garland Publishing, Inc., 1994.

Maizlish, Stephen E. and John G. Kushma, eds. *Essays on American Antebellum Politics, 1840-1860.* College Station, Tex.: Texas A&M University Press for the University of Texas at Arlington, 1982.

Marzalek, John F. and Wilson D. Miscamble, eds. *American Political History: Essays on the State of the Discipline.* Notre Dame, Ind.: University of Notre Dame Press, 1997.

Mattson, Kevin. *Creating a Democratic Public: The Struggle for Urban Participatory Democracy During the Progressive Period.* University Park, Pa.: Pennsylvania State University Press, 1998.

McClure, A. K. *Our Presidents and How We Make Them.* New York: Harper & Brothers Publishers, 1900.

McCormick, Richard L. "The Discovery that Business Corrupts Politics: A Reappraisal of the Origins of Progressivism." *The American Historical Review* 86 (April 1981): 247-74.

McCormick, Richard L. "Ethno-Cultural Interpretations of Nineteenth-Century American Voting Behavior." *Political Science Quarterly* 89 (June 1974): 351-77.

McCormick, Richard L. *From Realignment to Reform: Political Change in New York State, 1893-1910.* Ithaca, N.Y.: Cornell University Press, 1981.

McCormick, Richard L. "The Party Period and Public Policy: An Exploratory Hypothesis." *The Journal of American History* 66 (September 1979): 279-98.

McCormick, Richard L. *The Party Period and Public Policy: American Politics from the Age of Jackson to the Progressive Era.* New York: Oxford University Press, 1986.

McCormick, Richard L., ed. *Political Parties and the Modern State.* New Brunswick, N.J.: Rutgers University Press, 1984.

McCormick, Richard P. *The Presidential Game: The Origins of American Presidential Politics*. New York: Oxford University Press, 1982.

McCormick, Richard P. *The Second American Party System: Party Formation in the Jacksonian Era*. Chapel Hill: University of North Carolina Press, 1966.

McCullough, David. *John Adams*. New York: Simon and Schuster, 2001.

McGerr, Michael E. *The Decline of Popular Politics: The American North, 1865-1928*. New York: Oxford University Press, 1986.

McGerr, Michael E. "Political Style and Women's Power, 1830-1930." *Journal of American History* 77 (Dec. 1990): 864-85.

McGinniss, Joe. *The Selling of the President, 1968*. New York: Trident Press, 1969.

McGlen, Nancy M. and Karen O'Connor. *Women, Politics, and American Society*. Inglewood Cliffs, N.J.: Prentice Hall, 1995.

McSeveney, Samuel T. *The Politics of Depression: Political Behavior in the Northeast, 1893-1896*. New York: Oxford University Press, 1972.

Mead, Rebecca J. *How the Vote Was Won: Woman Suffrage in the Western United States, 1868-1914*. New York: New York University Press, 2003.

Melder, Keith. *Hail to the Candidate: Presidential Campaigns from Banners to Broadcasts*. Washington, D.C.: The Smithsonian Institute, 1992.

Miller, Warren E., and J. Merrill Shanks. *The New American Voter*. Cambridge, Mass.: Harvard University Press, 1996.

Morone, James A. *The Democratic Wish: Popular Participation and the Limits of American Government*. New York: Basic Books, 1990.

Morreale, Joanne. *The Presidential Campaign Film: A Critical History*. Westport, Conn.: Praeger, 1993.

Morris, Edmund. *The Rise of Theodore Roosevelt*. New York: Coward, McCann, & Geoghegan, 1979.

Morris, Edmund. *Theodore Rex*. New York: Random House, 2001.

Mulkern, John L. *The Know-Nothing Party in Massachusetts: The Rise and Fall of a People's Movement*. Boston: Northeastern University Press, 1990.

Nardulli, Peter F. "A Normal Vote Approach to Electoral Change: Presidential Elections, 1828-1984." *Political Behavior* 16 (Dec. 1994): 467-503.

Newman, Bruce I. *The Mass Marketing of Politics: Democracy in an Age of Manufactured Images*. Thousand Oaks, Calif.: Sage Publications, 1999.

Newman, Simon T. *Parades and the Politics of the Street: Festive Culture in the Early American Republic*. Philadelphia: University of Pennsylvania Press, 1997.

Noll, Mark A., ed. *Religion and American Politics: From the Colonial Period to the 1980s*. New York: Oxford University Press, 1990.

Norton, A. Banning. *The Great Revolution of 1840: Reminiscences of the Log Cabin and Hard Cider Campaign*. Mt. Vernon, Ohio and Dallas, Tex.: A. B. Norton and Co., 1888.

Nugent, Walter T.K. "Politics from Reconstruction to 1900," in William H. Cartwright and Richard L. Watson, Jr., eds., *The Reinterpretation of American History and Culture*. Washington, D.C.: National Council for the Social Studies, 1973, pp. 377-99.

Oldroyd, Osborne H. *Lincoln's Campaign: or, The Political Revolution of 1860*. Chicago: Laird and Lee, 1896.

Patterson, Thomas E. *The Mass Media Election: How Americans Choose Their President*. New York: Praeger, 1980.

Patterson, Thomas E. *The Vanishing Voter: Public Involvement in an Age of Uncertainty*. New York: Alfred A. Knopf, 2002.

Peek, George A., Jr. *The Political Writings of John Adams*. Indianapolis, Ind.: Bobbs-Merrill, 1954.

Pemberton, William E. *Exit with Honor: The Life and Presidency of Ronald Reagan*. Armonk, N.Y.: M.E. Sharpe, 1997.

Pessen, Edward. *The Log Cabin Myth: The Social Backgrounds of the Presidents*. New Haven, Conn.: Yale University Press, 1984.

Phillips, Kevin. *The Emerging Republican Majority*. New Rochelle, N.Y.: Arlington House, 1969.

Piven, Frances Fox, and Richard A. Cloward. *Why Americans Don't Vote*. New York: Pantheon Books, 1988.

Polsby, Nelson W., and Aaron B. Wildavsky. *Presidential Elections: Strategies of American Electoral Politics*. New York: Charles Scribner's Sons, 1964.

Pomper, Gerald M. with Susan S. Lederman. *Elections in America: Control and Influence in Democratic Politics*. 2nd ed. New York: Longman, 1980.

Presidential Elections since 1789. Washington, D.C.: Congressional Quarterly, Inc., 1987.

Pringle, Henry F. *Theodore Roosevelt: A Biography*. New York: Harcourt, Brace, and Company, 1931.

Re, Oh Jong. *Labor at the Polls: Union Voting in Presidential Elections, 1952-1976*. Amherst, Mass: University of Massachusetts Press, 1978.

Rhodehamel, John, ed. *George Washington: Writings*. New York: Library of America, 1997.

Rhodes, James Ford. *History of the United States from Hayes to McKinley, 1877-1896*. New York: The MacMillan Company, 1919.

Robinson, Claude E. *Straw Votes: A Study of Political Prediction*. New York: Columbia University Press, 1932.

Robinson, Edgar Eugene. *The Evolution of American Political Parties*. New York: Harcourt Brace and Company, 1924.

Robinson, Edgar Eugene. *The Presidential Vote, 1896-1932*. Stanford, Calif.: Stanford University Press, 1934.

Rogers, Donald W., ed. *Voting and the Spirit of American Democracy: Essays on the History of Voting and Voting Rights in America*. Urbana, Ill.: University of Illinois Press, 1992.

Rose, Richard, ed. *Electoral Behavior: A Comparative Handbook*. New York: Free Press, 1974.

Roseboom, Eugene H. *A Short History of Presidential Elections*. New York: Collier Books, 1957.

Rosenstone, Steven J., and John Mark Hansen. *Mobilization, Participation, and Democracy in America*. New York: MacMillan Publishing Co., 1993.

Rozell, Mark J., William D. Pederson, and Frank J. Williams, eds. *George Washington and the Origins of the American Presidency*. Westport, Conn.: Praeger, 2000.

Rubin, Bernard. *Political Television*. Belmont, Calif.: Wadsworth Publishing Co., 1967.

Russell, Francis. *The Shadow of Blooming Grove: Warren G. Harding in His Times*. New York: McGraw Hill, 1968.

Ryan, Mary P. *Women in Public: Between Banners and Ballots, 1825-1880*. Baltimore: Johns Hopkins University Press, 1990.

Sabato, Larry J. *The Rise of Political Consultants: New Ways of Winning Elections*. New York: Basic Books, 1981.

Salmore, Stephen, and Barbara G. Salmore. *Candidates, Parties, and Campaigns: Electoral Politics in America*. Washington, D.C.: Congressional Quarterly, Inc., 1985.

Sanbonmatsu, Kira. *Democrats, Republicans, and the Politics of Women's Place*. Ann Arbor, Mich.: University of Michigan Press, 2002.

Sapiro, Virginia. *The Political Integration of Women: Roles, Socialization, and Politics*. Urbana, Ill.: University of Illinois Press, 1983.

Schlesinger, Arthur M., Jr., ed. *The Coming to Power: Critical Presidential Elections in American History*. New York: Chelsea House Publishers, 1972.

Schlesinger, Arthur M., Jr., ed. *History of American Presidential Elections, 1789-1968.* 4 vols. New York: Chelsea House Publishers, 1971.

Schlesinger, Arthur M., Jr., ed. *History of U.S. Political Parties.* 4 vols. New York: Chelsea House Publishers, 1973.

Schlesinger, Arthur M., Jr., ed. *Running for President, The Candidates and Their Images, 1789-1896.* 2 vols. New York: Simon & Schuster, 1994.

Schramm, Martin. *The Great American Video Game: Presidential Politics in the Television Age.* New York: William Morrow and Company, 1987.

Schutz, Charles E. *Political Humor: From Aristophanes to Sam Ervin.* Rutherford, N.J.: Fairleigh Dickinson Press, 1977.

Schwarz, Barry. *George Washington: The Making of an American Symbol.* New York: Free Press, 1987.

Seldes, Gilbert Vivian. *The Great Audience.* New York: Viking Press, 1950.

Selecting the President: From 1789 to 1996. Washington, D.C.: Congressional Quarterly, Inc., 1997.

Shafer, Byron E. and Anthony J. Badger, eds. *Contesting Democracy: Substance and Structure in American Political History, 1775-2000.* Lawrence, Kans.: University Press of Kansas, 2001.

Sievers, Harry J. *Benjamin Harrison.* 3 vols. Chicago: H. Regnery Co., 1952-1968.

Silbey, Joel H., ed. *The American Party Battle: Election Campaign Pamphlets, 1828-1876.* Cambridge, Mass.: Harvard University Press, 1999.

Silbey, Joel H. *The American Political Nation, 1838-1893.* Stanford, Calif.: Stanford University Press, 1991.

Silbey, Joel H., Allan G. Bogue, and William H. Flanigan, eds. *The History of American Electoral Behavior.* Princeton, N.J.: Princeton University Press, 1978.

Silbey, Joel H. *The Partisan Imperative: The Dynamics of American Politics Before the Civil War.* New York: Oxford University Press, 1985.

Silbey, Joel H. "Party Organization in Nineteenth-Century America," in L. Sandy Maisel, and William G. Shade, *Parties and Politics in American History: A Reader.* New York: Garland Publishing, Inc., 1994, pp. 83-101.

Silbey, Joel H. *Political Ideology and Voting Behavior in the Age of Jackson.* Inglewood Cliffs, N.J.: Prentice-Hall, Inc., 1974.

Silbey, Joel H. *A Respectable Minority: The Democratic Party in the Civil War Era, 1860-1868.* New York: W. W. Norton, 1977.

Silbey, Joel H. *The Shrine of Party: Congressional Voting Behavior, 1841-1852.* Pittsburgh: University of Pittsburgh Press, 1967.

Skocpol, Theda. *Protecting Soldiers and Mothers: The Political Origins of Social Policy in the United States.* Cambridge, Mass.: Harvard University Press, 1992.

Skowronek, Stephen. *The Politics Presidents Make: Leadership from John Adams to George Bush.* Cambridge, Mass.: Belknap Press, 1993.

Smallwood, Frank. *The Other Candidates: Third Parties in Presidential Elections.* Hanover, N.H.: University Press of New England, 1983.

Sorauf, Frank J. *Party Politics in America.* Boston: Little, Brown, 1968.

Spero, Robert. *The Duping of the American Voter: Dishonesty & Deception in Presidential Television Advertising.* New York: Lippincott & Crowell, 1980.

Stanwick, Kathy, and Christine Li. *The Political Participation of Women in the United States: A Selected Bibliography, 1950-1976.* Metuchen, N.J.: The Scarecrow Press, 1977.

Statistics of the Congressional Election of November, 5, 2002, Showing the Vote Cast for Each Nominee for United States Senator, Representative, and Delegate to the One Hundred Eighth Congress (Washington, D.C., 2003), http://clerk.house.gov.

Steinfeld, Robert J. "Property and Suffrage in the Early American Republic." *Stanford Law Review* 41 (Jan. 1989): 335-76.

Streb, Matthew J. *The New Electoral Politics of Race.* Tuscaloosa, Ala.: University of Alabama Press, 2002.

Sullivan, Edmund B. *American Political Badges and Medalets, 1789-1892.* Lawrence, Mass.: Quarterman Publications, Inc., 1981.

Sullivan, Edmund B. *American Political Ribbons and Ribbon Badges, 1825-1981.* Lincoln, Mass.: Quarterman Publications, 1985.

Sullivan, Edmund B. *Collecting Political Americana.* New York: Crown Publishers, Inc., 1980.

Sullivan, Edmund B. *Hell-Bent for the White House.* Stamford, Conn.: Champion International Corp., 1988.

Takaki, Ronald T. *Iron Cages: Race and Culture in Nineteenth-Century America.* New York: Alfred A. Knopf, 1979.

Tannenbaum, Percy H., and Leslie J. Kostrich. *Turned-On T.V./Turned-Off Voters: Policy Options for Election Projections.* Beverly Hills, Calif.: Sage Publications, 1983.

Taylor, John M. *Garfield of Ohio: The Available Man.* New York: W. W. Norton, 1970.

Terborg-Penn, Rosalyn. *African American Women and the Struggle for the Vote, 1850-1920.* Bloomington, Ind.: Indiana University Press, 1998.

Thomas, G. Scott. *The Pursuit of the White House: A Handbook of Presidential Election Statistics and History.* Westport, Conn.: Greenwood Press, 1987.

Thomson, Charles A. H. *Television and Presidential Politics: The Experience in 1952 and the Problems Ahead.* Washington, D.C.: The Brookings Institution, 1956.

Turner, Victor. *Celebration: Studies in Festivity and Ritual.* Washington, D.C.: Smithsonian Institution Press, 1982.

U.S. Census Bureau. *Statistical Abstract of the United States: 2002.* Washington, D.C.: G.P.O., 2002.

U.S. Department of Commerce, Economics and Statistics Administration, U.S. Census Bureau. "Voting and Registration in the Election of November 2000." Washington, D.C.: G.P.O., 2002.

Vermeer, Jan Pons, ed. *Campaigns in the News: Mass Media and Congressional Elections.* New York: Greenwood Press, 1987.

Ware, Susan. *Beyond Suffrage: Women and the New Deal.* Cambridge, Mass.: Harvard University Press, 1981.

Weiss, Nancy J. *Farewell to the Party of Lincoln: Black Politics in the Age of FDR.* Princeton, N.J.: Princeton University Press, 1983.

West, Darrell M. *Air Wars: Television Advertising in Election Campaigns, 1952-1992.* Washington, D.C.: Congressional Quarterly, Inc., 1993.

Wheeler, Marjorie Spruill. *New Women of the New South: The Leaders of the Woman Suffrage Movement in the Southern States.* New York: Oxford University Press, 1993.

White, Theodore H. *America in Search of Itself: The Making of the President, 1956-1980.* New York: Harper & Row, 1982.

White, Theodore H. *The Making of the President, 1960.* New York: Athaneum Press, 1961.

White, Theodore H. *The Making of the President, 1964.* New York: Athaneum Press, 1965.

White, Theodore H. *The Making of the President, 1968.* New York: Athaneum Press, 1969.

White, Theodore H. *The Making of the President, 1972.* New York: Athaneum Publishers, 1973.

Wiebe, Robert H. *Self-Rule: A Cultural History of American Democracy.* Chicago: University of Chicago Press, 1995.

Wiebe, Robert H. *The Opening of American Society: From the Adoption of the Constitution to the Eve of Disunion.* New York: Alfred A. Knopf, 1984.

Williams, R. Hal. "'Dry Bones and Dead Language': The Democratic Party," in H. Wayne Morgan, ed., *The Gilded Age: A Reappraisal*. Syracuse: Syracuse University Press, 1970, pp. 129-48.

Williams, R. Hal. "The Politics of the Gilded Age," in John F. Marszlek and Wilson D. Miscamble, eds., *American Political History: Essays on the State of the Discipline*. Notre Dame, Ind.: University of Notre Dame Press, 1997, pp. 108-42.

Williams, R. Hal. *The Democratic Party and California Politics, 1880-1896*. Stanford, Calif.: Stanford University Press, 1973.

Williams, R. Hal. *Years of Decision: American Politics in the 1890s*. New York: John Wiley & Sons, 1978.

Williamson, Chilton. *American Suffrage: From Property to Democracy, 1760-1860*. Princeton, N.J.: Princeton University Press, 1960.

Witcover, Jules. *Party of the People, A History of the Democrats*. New York: Random House, 2003.

FROM GEORGE TO GEORGE: PRESIDENTIAL ELECTIONS IN THE UNITED STATES FROM 1789 TO THE PRESENT was produced in an edition of one thousand copies in August, 2004. Designed and typeset by Jace Graf, Cloverleaf Studio, Austin, Texas, using Sabon and Allegheny types. Original photography by Jon Speck, Bridwell Library. Additional photography courtesy of Hillsman S. Jackson, SMU Office of Public Affairs; Museum of American Political Life, University of Hartford; Amon Carter Museum; and Smithsonian Institution, National Museum of American History, Behring Center. Printed and bound by The Studley Press, Dalton, Massachusetts.